W9-CRB-393

Molecular Connectivity in
Structure-Activity Analysis

CHEMOMETRICS SERIES

Series Editor: **Dr. D. Bawden**
Pfizer Central Research, Sandwich, Kent, England

1. Distance Geometry and Conformational Calculations
    G. M. Crippen

2. Clustering of Large Data Sets
    Jure Zupan

3. Multivariate Data Analysis in Industrial Practice
    Paul J. Lewi

4. Correlation Analysis of Organic Reactivity: With particular
    reference to multiple regression
    John Shorter

5. Information Theoretic Indices for Characterization of Chemical
    Structures
    Danail Bonchev

6. Logical and Combinatorial Algorithms for Drug Design
    V. E. Golender *and* **A. B. Rozenblit**

7. Minimum Steric Difference
    The MTD method for QSAR studies
    Z. Simon, A. Chiriac, S. Holban, D. Ciubotaru *and* **G. I. Mihalas**

8. Analytical Measurement and Information
    Advances in the information theoretic approach to chemical analyses
    K. Eckschlager *and* **V. Štěpánek**

9. Molecular Connectivity in Structure-Activity Analysis
    Lemont B. Kier *and* **Lowell H. Hall**

Molecular Connectivity in Structure-Activity Analysis

Lemont B. Kier
Virginia Commonwealth University, USA
and
Lowell H. Hall
Eastern Nazarene College, USA

RESEARCH STUDIES PRESS LTD.
Letchworth, Hertfordshire, England

JOHN WILEY & SONS INC.
New York · Chichester · Toronto · Brisbane · Singapore

7351-6466

CHEMISTRY

RESEARCH STUDIES PRESS LTD.
58B Station Road, Letchworth, Herts. SG6 3BE, England

Copyright © 1986, by Research Studies Press Ltd.

Marketing and Distribution:

Australia, New Zealand, South-east Asia:
Jacaranda-Wiley Ltd., Jacaranda Press
JOHN WILEY & SONS INC.
GPO Box 859, Brisbane, Queensland 4001, Australia

Canada:
JOHN WILEY & SONS CANADA LIMITED
22 Worcester Road, Rexdale, Ontario, Canada

Europe, Africa:
JOHN WILEY & SONS LIMITED
Baffins Lane, Chichester, West Sussex, England

North and South America and the rest of the world:
JOHN WILEY & SONS INC.
605 Third Avenue, New York, NY 10158, USA

Library of Congress Cataloging in Publication Data

Kier, Lemont B. (Lemont Burwell)
   Molecular connectivity in structure-activity analysis.

   (Chemometrics series; 9)
   Includes bibliographies and index.
   1. Structure-activity relationships (Biochemistry)
I. Hall, Lowell H., 1937–   . II. Title.   III. Series.
[DNLM: 1. Models, Molecular.   2. Structure-Activity
Relationship.   QV 744 K465m]
QP517.S85K54   1986   574.19'283   85-30019
ISBN 0 471 90983 1 (Wiley)

British Library Cataloguing in Publication Data

Kier, Lemont B.
   Molecular connectivity in structure-activity
   analysis.——(Chemometrics series; 9)
   1. Structure-activity relationships (Biochemistry)
   2. Molecules
I. Title   II. Hall, Lowell H.   III. Series
574.19'24   RM301.42

   ISBN 0 86380 039 4
   ISBN 0 471 90983 1 Wiley

   ISBN 0 86380 039 4 (Research Studies Press Ltd.)
   ISBN 0 471 90983 1 (John Wiley & Sons Inc.)

Printed in Great Britain by Short Run Press Ltd., Exeter

DEDICATED TO OUR WIVES

MARTHA L. KIER

AND

DORLA D. HALL

Preface

Nearly a decade has passed since the introduction of molecular connectivity as a new structure-based approach to biological quantitative structure-activity analysis (QSAR). Since that time many publications have demonstrated the applicability of this method to the analysis of physical properties and biological activity. It has been repeatedly shown that models in the form of QSAR equations can be found which permit a direct translation in terms of molecular structure. This interpretability is the essence of the molecular connectivity method.

A number of significant advances in the molecular connectivity methodology and its information significance have occurred over the past ten years. These advances have broadened the scope of the method and have strengthened the value of the results. Of particular note are the revelations that the index values are based on electron and orbital counts, leading to information about topology and electronic structure. This has greatly enhanced the meaning of the equation models and has provided a much firmer basis for the interpretations beyond the mere development of statistical relationships.

Several studies have shown the broad applicability of chi indexes using different statistical methods. Applications deal with multiple linear regression, including nonlinear models, nonlinear least squares, discriminant analysis and principal component analysis. Studies with random numbers indicate that models based on connectivity may be developed in such a way as to avoid the possibility of chance correlations.

We feel that the time has come to prepare a second book on molecular connectivity. The invitation to contribute to the Chemometrics Series is a welcomed opportunity to write a volume directed towards the QSAR practitioner. The basic formalism is developed from a chemist's perspective. The implications to molecular structure are presented and discussed. Statistical considerations are investigated. Practical strategies for implementation are presented with biological examples.

Chapter 1 develops the background and foundations of molecular connectivity. In Chapter 2 regression models with selected physicochemical properties demonstrate that molecular connectivity equations can be used as a basis for the estimation of property values. Chapter 3 develops information on the relation of connectivity indexes to molecular topology and spatial characteristics such as volume and skeletal arrangement. In chapter 4 electronic aspects of structure encoded in chi indexes are discussed, including electronegativity and substituent group influence. Chapter 5 briefly addresses some basic statistical considerations, including multiple linear regression, simple nonlinear models and problems in QSAR model development. In Chapter 6 several strategies for use of connectivity in QSAR are discussed. Chapter 7 presents a variety of biological studies with structural interpretation. Chapter 8 gives a listing of papers using molecular connectivity, organized under specific topics. In Chapter 9 we examine topics of current research calling for further exploration into the nature of molecular connectivity. We hope the overall result for the reader is a good preparation for use of molecular connectivity in QSAR investigations.

Over the past few years several of our colleagues and students have assisted us. At Eastern Nazarene College Chris Cove, Phil Clements, Doug Kitchen and Steve Henck have helped in many ways. At Virginia Commonwealth University we thank Pamela Baylor, Rosa Richardson, Mike Wickham and Cecial Culley for their help in word processing. Finally, we thank David Bawden for his editorial guidance.

Lowell H. Hall   Lemont B. Kier   October 4, 1985

Foreword

It is now eight years since I was privileged to visit the laboratory of Monty Kier for a period of sabbatical study. At that time, I considered myself quite well versed in the use of classical "Hansch Analysis" as an approach to correlation of biological with physicochemical data. My purpose was to learn from Professor Kier the elements of molecular orbital theory, and so to extend my capabilities as a QSAR practitioner to include the rational use of theoretical parameters, such as charge and energy, calculated by semi-empirical methods.

During that exciting period, I was drawn into many discussions with Monty Kier and Lowell Hall, concerning an approach to correlation analysis that was certainly much simpler in its mathematics than molecular orbital theory, and yet was fundamental in the sense that it was developed merely from counting valence electrons. The approach we discussed was molecular connectivity, and Kier and Hall had just published a first book on the topic. Clearly, they had rushed too early into print. They were still making discoveries about the use of the indexes. This new book shows that they have made many more discoveries since those days, and I know that more are yet to come.

Looking back, I remember my first feelings about molecular connectivity were of scepticism and suspicion. I was sceptical of their value, and suspicious of the statistics. I much preferred, and still do, the comfort of a physical model for drug action that could be accommodated within the framework of good correlations in measured properties such as log P or pKa, or in parameters reflecting changes in hydrophobic, electronic, or steric properties such as π, σ, or E_s. I believe I can appreciate the significance of such parameters.

The questions I have asked about molecular connectivity reflect my own bias as a physical organic chemist: What is chi really measuring? Is a correlation involving chi actually useful in diagnosis of mechanism of action? And does such a correlation aid the chemist to predict useful directions for further synthesis? This collection of studies on the properties of molecular connectivity indexes provides answers to the first question, and I believe will guide the reader in seeking his own answers to the other questions.

We must not be so entrenched in classical, physicochemical QSAR that we fail to develop, and understand, new methods and parameters. A criticism of the use of property-based data is that properties can so frequently be redundant parameters. Two or more structures in the same data-set can have the same log P value or same pKa. It is not possible, unless they be cis-trans or optical isomers, for them to have the same set of chi indexes. In QSAR development, the combination of chi indexes with appropriate physicochemical parameters is a laudable trend. To the serious, open-minded practitioner of QSAR I commend this book.

Michael S. Tute
Pfizer Central Research
Sandwich, Kent, U.K.
September 1985

Contents

1. ORIGINS OF MOLECULAR CONNECTIVITY 1

   1. The meaning of molecular structure. 1
   2. General approaches to structure description . . . 3
   3. The topological approach 7
     A. Randic branching index 8
     B. Other approaches 10
   4. Molecular connectivity 10
     A. The formalism 11
     B. Extended indexes. 12
     C. Unsaturation 15
     D. Heteroatoms 16
     E. Heteroatoms in higher quantum levels. . . . 18
     F. Heteroatoms in higher oxidation states . . . 19
   5. Summary 20
     Examples of calculations. 21
     References 23

2. RELATION TO PHYSICAL PROPERTIES 25

   1. Molar refraction 26
     A. Alkanes 26
     B. Alkyl benzenes 27
     C. Polarizability of a mixed data set . . . 28
   2. Water solubility 29
     A. Alcohols 29
     B. Halobenzenes 29
   3. Molar volume 30
     A. Alkanes 31
     B. Quaternary ammonium salts 31

4. Chromatographic retention data 32

   A. Alkanes 32

   B. Polyaromatic hydrocarbons 33

   C. Pyrazine carbothioamides 33

   D. Aliphatic alcohols 34

5. Thermodynamic properties 35

   A. Heat of atomization 35

   B. Heat of vaporization 36

6. Other properties 37

   A. Magnetic susceptibility 37

   B. Van der Waals equation constants 38

7. Summary 40

   References 41

3. TOPOLOGICAL INFORMATION 43

1. Information from ^1X and $^1X^v$ 43

   A. Relative degree of branching 43

   B. Molecular size 44

   C. Molecular volume 44

   D. Molecular surface area 48

   E. Topology of unsaturation and heteroatoms . . 50

2. Information from ^2X and $^2X^v$ 50

3. Information from ^3X_p 53

   A. Conformational possibilities 53

   B. Density analysis 57

   C. Flexibility 58

4. Information from $^4X_{pc}$ and $^4X^v_{pc}$ 59

   A. Calculation 59

   B. Orientation of ring substituents 61

   C. Length of ring substituents 61

   D. Heteroatom substituents 63

5. Higher order path indexes 63

6. Other connectivity indexes 65

   A. $^{3}X_{c}$ index 65

   B. Chain indexes 65

7. Summary 65

   References 67

4. ELECTRONIC INFORMATION 69

1. Electron counts from delta values . . . 69

2. Estimation of valence state electronegativity . . 70

3. Derivation of the bond index 75

4. Electronic information encoded in $^{1}X^{v}$ . . . 76

5. Group values of electronegativity . . . 79

   A. General formula 79

   B. Benzene substituent value 80

   C. Substituent effect through pi orbitals . . 80

   D. Lone pair electron effect 82

   E. Examples of calculations 83

   F. Prediction of Hammett substituent values . . 84

6. Quantitation of solvent polarity 88

   A. Solvent polarity 88

   B. Derivation of solvent polarity index . . 88

   C. Functional group number weighting . . . 90

7. A benzene-like or aromaticity index from chi . . 94

   A. Aromaticity and benzene-likeness . . . 94

   B. Derivation of an index of benzene-likeness . . 95

   C. B values of heterocycles 97

   D. General comments 99

8. $^{m}X - ^{m}X^{v}$ index for atom-specific properties . . 99

   A. The information in $^{m}X - ^{m}X^{v}$ 99

   B. Ionization potential 100

9. Summary 101

   References 101

5. STATISTICAL CONSIDERATIONS 103

   1. Introduction 103
   2. Statistical background 104
      A. Basic terms and definitions 104
      B. Linear models 107
      C. Least squares analysis of simple linear cases . 108
      D. Results and analysis 112
      E. Deletion of an outliner 117
   3. Multiple linear and simple nonlinear cases . . 119
      A. The general situation 119
      B. Simple nonlinear models 121
   4. Multivariate nonlinear models 123
   5. Selection of a model 127
   6. Selection of few variables from many 128
   7. Chance correlation 135
      A. Use of random numbers 135
      B. Statistical stability of the regression model . 138
   8. Conclusion 142
   References

6. STRATEGIES FOR THE USE OF MOLECULAR CONNECTIVITY . . 145

   1. Selection of chi indexes for regression . . . 145
      A. Alkyl sidechains 146
      B. Heteroatom substituents 148
   2. Abbreviation of molecular structure 150
   3. Substructure/subgraph analysis 152
   4. Non-linear equations 156
      A. A hyperbolic model 157
      B. A quadratic model 158
      C. A Gaussian model 159

5. Use of additional parameters 159
   A. Non-coded properties 160
   B. Hammett sigma values 161
   C. Molecular symmetry 161
   D. Indicator variables 164
   E. Other physical properties 165
6. Use of other statistical methods 165
   A. Total response surface optimization . . . 165
   B. Size and electronic effects 166
   C. Discriminant analysis 173
7. Conclusions 179
   References 180

7. APPLICATIONS TO DRUG STUDIES 183

1. Selection of data for QSAR analyses 184
2. Study of ecotoxicological behavior 185
3. The QSAR of flavor threshold 186
4. QSAR of general anesthetics 189
5. QSAR of muscarinic antagonists 192
   A. Random number analysis 194
   B. Equation analysis 195
   C. Onium group fragment 196
   D. Bulky group fragment 197
   E. Prediction of antagonist affinities . . . 197
   F. Prediction of agonist affinities 198
   G. General comments 198
6. Hallucinogenic potency 200
   A. Chance correlation with random numbers . . 200
   B. Analysis of equation terms 201
7. QSAR of monoamine oxidase inhibitors 207
8. Discriminant analysis of taste 209
   A. Structural analyses and discrimination analysis . 209
   B. Discussion 210

9. QSAR of heterocycle toxicity 214

10. Antiviral QSAR using fragments 217

    A. Data set and regression analysis 217

    B. Structure analysis 219

    C. Conclusions 222

11. General summary 222

    References 223

8. PUBLISHED STUDIES USING MOLECULAR CONNECTIVITY . . 225

1. Methodology and interpretation 226

2. Application to physicochemical properties . . . 228

    A. General papers 228

    B. Chromatography 230

    C. Partition coefficient and solubility . . . 235

3. Biological activity 236

    A. General applications 236

    B. Anesthetics 238

    C. Flavor, odor, taste 239

    D. Psychomimetic and hallucinogenic activity . . 240

    E. Toxicological and environmental applications . 240

    F. Applications using classification methods . . 242

    G. Carcinogenesis and mutagenesis 243

    H. Antimicrobial and antibacterial 243

    I. Other applications 244

9. FUTURE DIRECTIONS OF MOLECULAR CONNECTIVITY . . . 247

1. The algorithm for $^2\chi$ 247

2. The value for fluorine 248

3. Valence delta values for third quantum level atoms . 249

4. Valence deltas for higher oxidation states . . . 250

5. Molecular shape 250

6. A chemical reaction index for information storage . 251

7. Structure interpretation from combinations of chi indexes 252

8. Direct use of sum and difference delta values . . 254

9. Connectivity indexes and property estimations . . 255

    References 256

AUTHOR INDEX 257

SUBJECT INDEX 259

CHAPTER 1
Origins of Molecular Connectivity

1. The Meaning of Molecular Structure

A major focus of scientific inquiry is the generation of information about the form and function of matter and their interrelation. Within the framework of the chemical sciences this dualism is usually expressed as the structure of molecules and their properties. The emergence of chemistry as a science has been due in part to the progress made in discovering atomic and molecular properties and accurately quantifying their relative values. A parallel achievement has been the efforts to categorize atoms or molecules systematically according to common features, called structure, and to relate these assignments to the values of measured properties. This has been described as quantitative structure–activity relationships (QSAR).

A property or activity of a molecule is a characteristic which can be determined or measured. By carefully subjecting molecules to a form of energy, numerical values are obtained with precision. Repeated subjection of a molecule to such an assault gives numerical measurements which are highly reproducible. By defining the physical events underway in such a process, we arrive at a phenomenon which we call a property. A profile of properties with precise numerical values becomes an integral part of the description of any molecule. Thus, acetone has a boiling point, molar refraction, viscosity, etc. which in the aggregate can be used to define a collection of molecules with a manifold of properties.

What is the information that we actually have from such a manifold? We can state clearly the properties of acetone under defined conditions, in other words its function. Information about its form or structure does not emerge directly from physical property measurements. The structure is inferred from these measurements because the properties are a consequence of the structure. It is truly a separate characteristic, another face of the dualism of matter, this information describing structure.

What is molecular structure? The chemist has a certain intuition, learned early in his exposure to the discipline, from which he derives communication about and familiarity with molecules. It may be useful to pause here and elaborate upon the common view of molecular structure.

In contrast to measured physical properties, the information associated with structure permits a mental construct, a picture, an image of the molecule which we can manipulate, rearrange or alter, governed only by the limits of our imagination. This conceptual freedom is denied us by the basic nature of a physical property.

At the molecular level, we can list a few characteristics associated with the definition of structure. This information includes: (1) the total number of atoms; (2) the number of different kinds of atoms; and, (3) the linking pattern or bonding scheme of atoms. It is evident that these three elements of structural information form the bases of the most common kind of communication in chemistry, the depiction of a molecule as a graphic structural formula or, more familiarly, the structural formula. It is possible to write a few symbols embodying these three elements of information, and every chemist in the world will know we are speaking of acetone, or whatever. We are at the level of describing a molecule in a semi-quantitative, pictorial way.

With the advent of quantum mechanics, it is possible to assess the probable positions of electrons and nuclear masses and thereby arrive at numerical values associated with each atom in a molecule. In fact, we have so much information that a mental image of the molecule, so treated, may be blurred. Nevertheless quantum mechanics has permitted great strides toward the goal of relating structure to properties.

Any definition of molecular structure can be viewed as being located somewhere in a spectrum of complexity, ranging from a quantum mechanical description down to some simple count of atoms. The familiar structural formula appears to afford a great potential for quantification because of the chemist's familiarity with it and the intuition that it evokes. The conversion of the structural formula into numerical values or indexes which encode structural information is thus a worthy goal. Indexes based on this graphic depiction afford a potential opportunity to compare molecular structures, store and classify, and relate structures to properties. Some progress along these lines has been made with a significant contribution being the general structure description called molecular connectivity (Kier and Hall, 1976).

2. General Approaches to Structure Description

There are two general aspects of structure which can be identified. In the first, the identities of atoms and their connections form one set of information about molecular structure commonly called the topology of the molecule. The second includes various three dimensional aspects called the molecular topography. Characteristics such as size, shape, volume, and surface area, however defined, are directly dependent on the three dimensional topography.

Generally, the properties of a molecule are dependent upon the three dimensional structure; however, the three dimensional molecular geometry depends on the molecular topology, that is, the nature of the individual atoms and the bonded connections between them. Because of the relationship between bond types and characteristics such as bond strength, length and polarity, it is expected that there are relationships between topology and properties. To the extent that the bonding scheme, as reflected in the molecular topology description, controls three dimensional geometry (topography) and the resulting properties, then properties must depend upon the molecular topology. For these reasons it is most useful to explore methods to represent molecular structure in the topological sense.

In our discussion, the term molecular structure includes the set of atom identifications and the connections between them. The connections are established through covalent bonds within the molecular skeleton. Other effects such as internal hydrogen bonds are not considered as connections and are handled in an alternate manner. In fact, only the molecular skeleton is considered; the presence of hydrogen atoms is not explicitly included, but implied in the general formulation of molecular indexes. The starting point in representing molecular structure is the molecular skeleton, often called the hydrogen-suppressed graph. Figure 1 shows several molecular structure representations as familiar molecular skeletons. Hydrogen atoms are shown only on heteroatoms for purposes of clear identification of the group.

Our objective in developing methods of quantitative structure description is to be able to relate chemical and biological properties to molecular structure. It should be noted that many properties have a fundamental additive nature. The property value may be obtained as a simple sum of atom or group values. Familiar examples include heat of formation of alkanes, molar refraction of alkyl halides, and the partition coefficient of alcohols. These additive schemes are quite satisfactory for straight chain compounds. For these structures, the property value is simply the sum of the contributions from each atom.

The constitutive nature of properties is revealed when values are examined for branched alkane isomers, heteroatom position isomers, or benzene ring substituent isomers. In these cases, property values depend upon the detailed arrangement of the atoms and the

a $CH_3CH_2CH_2CH_2CH_3$

b $CH_3CH(CH_3)CH_2CH_3$

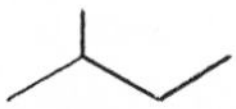

c $CH_3CH(CH_3)CH_2OH$

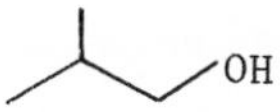

d $CH_3CH(CH_3)OCH_3$

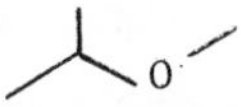

e $ClCH(CH_3)CH_2NH_2$

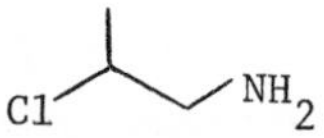

f $CH_2CH_2CH_2CH_2CH_2$

$$\begin{pmatrix} 0 & 1 & 0 & 0 & 0 \\ 1 & 0 & 1 & 0 & 0 \\ 0 & 1 & 0 & 1 & 0 \\ 0 & 0 & 1 & 0 & 1 \\ 0 & 0 & 0 & 1 & 0 \end{pmatrix} \quad \begin{pmatrix} 0 & 1 & 1 & 1 & 0 \\ 1 & 0 & 0 & 0 & 0 \\ 1 & 0 & 0 & 0 & 0 \\ 1 & 0 & 0 & 0 & 1 \\ 0 & 0 & 0 & 1 & 0 \end{pmatrix} \quad \begin{pmatrix} 0 & 1 & 0 & 0 & 1 \\ 1 & 0 & 1 & 0 & 0 \\ 0 & 1 & 0 & 1 & 0 \\ 0 & 0 & 1 & 0 & 1 \\ 1 & 0 & 0 & 1 & 0 \end{pmatrix}$$

    (a)   (b,c,d,e)   (f)   Connection Matrices

$$\begin{pmatrix} 0 & 1 & 2 & 3 & 4 \\ 1 & 0 & 1 & 2 & 3 \\ 2 & 1 & 0 & 1 & 2 \\ 3 & 2 & 1 & 0 & 1 \\ 4 & 3 & 2 & 1 & 0 \end{pmatrix} \quad \begin{pmatrix} 0 & 1 & 1 & 1 & 2 \\ 1 & 0 & 2 & 2 & 3 \\ 1 & 2 & 0 & 2 & 3 \\ 1 & 2 & 2 & 0 & 1 \\ 2 & 3 & 3 & 1 & 0 \end{pmatrix} \quad \begin{pmatrix} 0 & 1 & 2 & 2 & 1 \\ 1 & 0 & 1 & 2 & 2 \\ 2 & 1 & 0 & 1 & 2 \\ 2 & 2 & 1 & 0 & 1 \\ 1 & 2 & 2 & 1 & 0 \end{pmatrix}$$

    (a)   (b,c,d,e)   (f)   Distance Matrices

FIGURE 1.   Structural formulae, graphs and connection and distance matrices for several molecules.

bonds (molecular constitution), presumably because aspects such as size and shape as well as electronic structure depend upon such molecular structure considerations. Molar refraction may vary only a few percent for alkane isomers, heat of formation several percent for alcohols, boiling point 20 – 30% for alcohols, and an order of magnitude for ester water solubility. In any event, there is a measurable and significant dependence of properties on molecular structure, a dependence that appears related to molecular topology.

The simple summation is inadequate when skeletal structure varies in a nonhomologous way. For normal alkane properties, the count of carbon atoms is frequently sufficient; however, for alkane isomers there are ten possible bond types, and some properties, such as heat of formation, require all ten for close estimation. Fajans (1920) recognized the need for including information on atom bonding environments in estimation methods for heat of formation. Klages (1949) directed attention to the constitutive nature of heats of hydrogenation, by introducing terms for tertiary and quaternary carbon atoms in addition to terms for rings. Vogel (1948) devised an additive and constitutive scheme for molar refractivity. Pauling (1960) addressed the problem from the quantum mechanical point of view. Franklin (1949), Allen (1939), and Laidler (1956) each developed schemes for thermodynamic properties by making use of the number and nature of neighboring atoms in estimating a value for the bond.

These schemes became more and more elaborate. Introducing more and more parameters, Somayajulu and Zwolinski (1966) systematized the general approach and developed complex methods utilizing many additive and constituitive terms. As a result, rather accurate estimations may be made from large sets of empirical parameters for many physicochemical properties. Because of the large number of parameters introduced by these methods, another line of approach has also been investigated. In these methods, a more direct appeal is made to the information resident in the structure of the molecular skeleton. These approaches are the forerunners to the method called molecular connectivity, described in this book.

3. The Topological Approach

We begin this discussion with methods for representation of the connections in the skeleton, since the earliest approaches to topology either ignored the presence of heteroatoms or dealt primarily with saturated hydrocarbons. The most basic element in the molecular structure is the existence of a connection or a chemical bond between a pair of atoms, said to be adjacent. The whole set of connections may be conveniently represented in matrix form. Several examples are given as part of Fig. 1. The same information is also contained in what is called the connection table or the connectivity matrix.

Once the set of connections is written in matrix form, certain information can be extracted. One characteristic of a skeletal atom is the number of connected neighbors in the skeleton. This quantity, called the vertex degree or valence, is equal to the number of sigma bonds involving that atom, excluding bonds to hydrogen atoms. This number, δ_i, for atom i is equal to the number of nonzero elements in row i (or column i) in the connectivity matrix. For example, in the connectivity matrix in Fig. 1a, there are two 1's in row 3; $\delta_3 = 2$. It can be shown that the number of nonzero entries in the whole matrix is twice the number of bonds or connections in the molecular skeleton.

Distance information can be summarized in matrix form. The set of topological distances is called the distance matrix. It can be constructed from an examination of the molecular skeleton or the topological matrix. Examples are given in Fig. 1. The procedure for noncyclic skeletons (tree graphs) is straight forward. Cyclic skeletons present special problems since the distance between two atoms may, in general, be traversed along more than one path. The definition of topological distance is the number of connections in the shortest path between two atoms. The distance matrix has served some useful purposes, but it is limited due to the information lost for cyclic structures.

From the discussion of molecular structure and topology it is now possible to define the term topological or structural index as a count of selected topological features. Examples of commonly used structure indexes include total number of skeletal atoms or bonds, the number of bonds or atoms of a given type, number of double bonds or number of double bonds exo to a certain ring, number of rings, number of bridgehead carbons, number of hydrogen atoms alpha (adjacent) to another structure such as an aromatic ring or a carbonyl group, etc. This concept has been greatly expanded in recent years.

A. Randic Branching Index

Randic (1975) addressed the problem of the relative degree of branching among alkanes and how this attribute influenced certain physical properties. The study was built around an intention to rank order isomeric alkanes. In the alkane skeletons the degree of branching at each carbon, or the number of adjacent carbons, is a cardinal number associated with that atom. Each formal carbon-carbon bond is therefore describable by a pair of numbers, which are counts of the number of adjacent atoms linked to each carbon atom forming the bond. In alkanes the maximum number of adjacent atoms around a carbon atom is four; the minimum is one. There are ten different types or sets of bonds in alkanes:

$(1,1)$, $(1,2)$, $(1,3)$, $(1,4)$, $(2,2)$, $(2,3)$, $(2,4)$, $(3,3)$, $(3,4)$, $(4,4)$.

The higher the numbers in the set, the greater the branching found at one or the other carbon atom, or both, forming the bond. If these bond description sets could be converted to real numbers and then combined in some way over the entire molecule, an index related to branching could be at hand for alkanes.

Randic regarded the sets of bond descriptors for different alkanes in an isomeric series as inequalities based on the degree of branching. One algorithm which converts each set into a number and preserves the inequalities between isomeric alkanes is the product of the atom adjacency values within the set, taken to the -0.5 power. The sum of these numbers over all bonds in the molecule yields an index associated with each molecule. The greater the degree of branching in a molecule of an isomeric series, the larger will be some numbers in sets describing these bonds. The algorithm results in lower numerical values of the index for molecules with greater branching.

To illustrate this scheme, consider the isopentane skeleton. Each carbon atom is assigned a cardinal number which is a count of all adjacent or bonded carbon atoms.

The molecule is now dissected into bonds described by the adjacency numbers of the two atoms forming the bond:

$$(1,3), \ (1,3), \ (3,2), \ (2,1)$$

These bond descriptions are converted into a real number by taking the product within each parenthesis. An index is derived by taking the reciprocal square root of this product. The numbers are then summed over all subsets to give a numerical value associated with that molecule.

$$\text{index}: \quad (1 \cdot 3), \ (1 \cdot 3), \ (3 \cdot 2), \ (2 \cdot 1)$$
$$= \quad (0.577) + (0.577) + (0.408) + (0.707)$$
$$\text{index} = \quad 2.270$$

The branching index, as Randic called this last number, decreases in value among isomeric alkanes in parallel with what may be viewed as an increase in branching. This index was found to parallel closely the boiling point, Kovats constants, and a calculated surface area. A direct comparison between the Randic branching index and other topological indexes was reported by Amidon and Anik (1976). The Randic index appears to predict the boiling points of alkanes more closely.

From a conceptual point of view, only the Randic index takes into account the bonding or adjacency degree among carbons in alkanes. Some vital information of a non-empirical nature is built into the formulation. Furthermore, the algorithm emphasizes the existence of bonds; thus, this fundamental piece of chemical reality is also inherent in the scheme. With the explicit consideration of atoms and bonds as part of the algorithm, the way was made clear for major developments to include consideration of unsaturation and heteroatoms in a more comprehensive and useful molecular structure index.

B. Other Approaches

A number of structure-based approaches has appeared in the literature. Some have been used to a limited extent in QSAR analyses and are worth further study. For more background in this subject, the reader is referred to a good review by Bawden (1983).

4. Molecular Connectivity

Kier and Hall recognized in the Randic scheme the basic elements for the development of a general method to describe organic molecular structure in terms of the familiar molecular features, atoms and bonds. In a series of early papers, a formalism was adopted and the method extended to consider unsaturation, heteroatoms, and extended bond analyses. Each of these features will be elaborated upon in this section.

A. The Formalism

The term "molecular connectivity" was adopted by Kier and Hall (1975) as a descriptive title for the general method leading to indexes derived from the molecular structure. The initial assumption is made that there resides in the structural formula sufficient information so that an index, based upon non-empirical counts of atoms, can be calculated.

In the simplest form of the index, the structural formula is written down as a molecular skeleton in which all atoms are identical. Hydrogens are not included. The suppression of hydrogens in this simple case can be shown not to result in the loss of information since the number of hydrogens is related to the carbon valence minus the number of adjacent carbon atoms. Each carbon atom is then designated by a cardinal number which is a count of the number of adjacent carbon atoms. This count of adjacent or formally bonded carbons is called the delta value, δ. The molecular skeleton is then dissected into all constituent bonds, each designated by the two carbons, i and j, forming the bond. Using the Randic algorithm, a value for each bond is computed; thus, $(\delta_i \delta_j)^{-0.5}$.

The molecular index is the simple sum of these bond values over the entire molecule. Kier and Hall adopted the Greek letter Chi as the designation of this index. The prefix 1 indicates that the index is for a one-bond dissection of the molecule. The consequence of this identification will become apparent later.

$$^1X = \Sigma\ (\delta_i \delta_j)^{-0.5} \tag{1}$$

So far, the examples chosen have been alkanes; hence, each skeleton atom has been an sp^3 carbon atom. The index may be extended to heteroatom-containing molecules if the count of adjacent atoms includes the heteroatom as though it were another carbon atom. Hydrogens bonded to a heteroatom are ignored as with carbon. The delta value for an oxygen atom in an alcohol is 1, and in an ether, 2. The connectivity index is calculated as previously described. For diethyl ether, the calculation is as follows:

$$^{1}\chi : \quad (1,2), \ (2,2), \ (2,2), \ (2,2), \ (1,2)$$
$$= \quad (0.707) + (0.500) + (0.500) + (0.500) + (0.707)$$
$$^{1}\chi = \quad 2.914$$

This is regarded as a simple case, ignoring other considerations of the heteroatom; hence, the connectivity index is called a simple connectivity index.

In a similar way, each carbon atom in butadiene is assigned a delta value reflecting the number of adjacent bonded carbon atoms. Thus, the hybrid state and multiple bonding is not considered in the calculation of the simple molecular connectivity index. More will be said on this issue later, but it should be obvious that some structural information is not captured by this simple treatment.

B. Extended Indexes

It seemed illogical that a single index could encode sufficient information about molecular structure to relate closely to physical properties which have a complex dependence on three-dimensional structure. An analogy in geometry requires that three dimensions be known in order to compute the volume of a prism. A satisfactory description of molecular structure requires the capability of expressing, numerically, relative structure in several dimensions, or in terms of several kinds of fragments of the molecule. Since the original algorithm is based upon the dissection of a molecule into one-bond fragments, it is possible that further dissection into two-bond, three-bond, and other fragments types may provide the dimensionality that would enchance the information content necessary to relate to molecular properties.

Accordingly Kier and Hall (1976) adopted a scheme whereby higher order dissection of the molecular skeleton became the basis of additional extended indexes. In the simplest case, the scheme involves the dissection of the molecular skeleton into all "two contiguous bond" fragments, in which the delta values are retained. For isopentane the two-bond dissection is as follows:

A term for each two-bond (three-contiguous atom) fragment is now computed using a modification of the algorithm, $(\delta_i \delta_j \delta_k)^{-0.5}$ as the general term. Therefore:

$$^2X = \Sigma \ (\delta_i \delta_j \delta_k)^{-0.5} \tag{2}$$

and a second order molecular connectivity index is defined. In the case of isopentane, above, the fragment terms used in the calculation are:

$$(1,3,1), \ (1,3,2), \ (1,3,2), \ (3,2,1)$$

The ^2X index is a sum of four fragment values. In the case of n-pentane, the molecule is dissected into only three two-bond fragments while the neopentane isomer dissects into six two-bond fragments. Clearly, a different pattern of structural information is possible from this index relative to ^1X. Higher order molecular connectivity indexes are now possible by dissection of any molecule into all possible m-bond fragments to be calculated and summed to give an ^mX_p index, where the subscript p denotes a contiguous path type of fragment.

In addition to these path fragments, one can envision the potential structural information to be derived from a dissection of a molecule into other commonly recurring features such as:

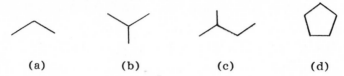

| (a) | (b) | (c) | (d) |

From graph theory, these fragments are called: (a) a path (2nd order); (b) a cluster (3rd order); (c) a path/cluster (4th order); and (d) a chain (5th order). The calculation of the index derived from each of these fragments in a molecule follows the same scheme as previously described. For the isopentane molecule, the third order cluster index, ^3X_c, is calculated from the single fragment described by the delta values $(1,3,1,2)$, where the subscript c indicates a cluster index. The pathcluster index, $^4X_{pc}$, for isopentane uses the entire molecule as the fragment, denoted by the delta values $(1,3,1,2,1)$. The n-pentane molecule has neither the cluster or path/cluster fragments; hence, the values of these indexes are zero.

The fragments described thus far have been composed of contiguous bonds in paths, clusters or chains (cycles). In the simplest case, a molecule may be decomposed into fragments of atoms which we denote as being of zero order. Using the delta values for atoms, the algorithm produces a series of terms, $\delta^{-0.5}$, for each atom fragment. The molecular connectivity index of the zeroth order is thus:

$$^0X = \Sigma\,(\,\delta\,)^{-0.5} \tag{3}$$

The index relates to atoms, not bonds, and must be viewed as reflecting structure at the atomic level in terms of the number of adjacent atoms dictating the delta value.

C. Unsaturation

The fact that butane and butadiene have the same delta values; hence, the same ^1X values, points up a basic limitation in what we have called the simple molecular connectivity index. If the information inherent in the butane and butadiene molecular structures is to be extracted more extensively, then a basically different formulation must be introduced into the original algorithm. Accordingly, Kier and Hall (1976) put forward a new rationale for the assignment of atom delta values. In this case, the assignment of the delta values is based on the explicit counting of each bond to an adjacent atom, irrespective of its type (suppressing hydrogen as usual). A double bond would be counted twice when adding up adjacent atoms. The butadiene molecule, therefore, would have the following delta values:

$$
\begin{array}{cccc}
2 & 3 & 3 & 2 \\
C = C & - C & = C
\end{array}
$$

This procedure takes explicit account of the valence of each carbon, or more precisely, of the hybrid state of the carbon atoms. This modified delta value is referred to as a valence delta, δ^V. The calculation proceeds as before to give a new type of molecular connectivity index based upon valence deltas. This index is called a $^1X^V$ or valence chi of the first order. The $^1X^V$ for butadiene is different from $^1X^V$ for butane, reflecting a different structure.

A general expression for this valence delta emerges:

$$
\delta^V = Z^V - h \tag{4}
$$

where Z^V is the number of valence electrons and h is the number of hydrogen atoms suppressed. It follows that each carbon atom of benzene would have $\delta^V = 3$ in valence chi calculations and $\delta = 2$ in simple chi calculations. It is also apparent that in an alkane all carbons have $\delta^V = \delta$.

D. Heteroatoms

The most important innovation in the development of this new structural paradigm was the treatment of heteroatoms, introduced by Kier and Hall (1976). This single feature elevated the original branching index from a theoretical curiosity, capable of dealing only with biologically uninteresting alkanes, to a powerful structural description capable of analyzing the structure-activity relationships among a host of biologically active molecules.

The heteroatom treatment hinges on the selection of appropriate delta values which reflect the structural differences in some logical way. The actual conception of the scheme was based upon the explicit count of adjacent bonded atoms (excluding hydrogen) plus a count of all pi and lone pair electrons. Thus, for oxygen in an alcohol, R-OH, the $\delta^V_{OH} = 5$. This is computed from the count of one adjacent carbon, plus four electrons in two lone pair orbitals. It is evident that the general equation 4, $\delta^V = Z^V - h$, presented under the unsaturation discussion, is used for the heteroatom for an alcohol oxygen atom: $\delta^V = 5$. Other second quantum level atoms in various hybrid states are shown in Table 1. The structural formula of a heteroatom molecule leads to a δ^V value which is characteristic, but not necessarily unique, for that heteroatom. The uniqueness arises from the influence of the heteroatom on atoms bonded to it. The nitrogen atoms in a nitrile and a tertiary amine both have $\delta^V = 5$; however, the tertiary amine nitrogen must be bonded to three atoms while the nitrile nitrogen can only be bonded to one other atom. The $(\delta_N \delta_j)^{-0.5}$ terms occur three times in computing $^1X^V$ for an amine, but only once for a nitrile. Thus the adjacency of the heteroatom along with its valency is encoded into the $^1X^V$ index. The fluorine atom in Table 1 is described in an indefinite way with regard to its hybrid state, although informed opinion is directed toward the view that it is very little hybridized. It will be shown in a later chapter that $\delta^V_F = 7$ reproduces the Pauling electronegativity estimate for this atom.

TABLE 1. Valence delta values for neutral, 2nd quantum level heteroatoms in various hybrid states.

Atom	Hybrid state	No. of H [a)]	Adjacent atoms δ	Valence electrons	Pi electrons	Lone pair electrons	δ^v
C	sp^3	3	1	4	0	0	1
		2	2	4	0	0	2
		1	3	4	0	0	3
		0	4	4	0	0	4
	sp^2	2	1	4	1	0	2
		1	2	4	1	0	3
		0	3	4	1	0	4
	sp	1	1	4	2	0	3
		0	2	4	2	0	4
N	sp^3	2	1	5	0	2	3
		1	2	5	0	2	4
		0	3	5	0	2	5
	sp^2	1	1	5	1	2	4
		0	2	5	1	2	5
	sp	0	1	5	2	2	5
O	sp^3	1	1	6	0	4	5
		0	2	6	0	4	6
	sp^2	0	1	6	1	4	6
F [b)]		0	1	7			7

a) The cases of CH_4, NH_3, H_2O and HF are not included.
b) Hybrid state not specified.

E. Heteroatoms - Higher Quantum Levels

The valence delta values are expressions of the electronic structure of the skeletal atoms in a molecule. The simple delta is a count of electrons in sigma orbitals whereas the valence delta is a count of all valence electrons. (Electrons in bonds to hydrogen are excluded in both cases).

When considering higher row atoms, specific account must be taken of the non-valence or core electrons. These core electrons play a strong and direct role in the size of atoms and indirectly influence such properties as ionization potential and electron affinity.

To take account of both valence and core electrons the valence delta value can be written as a fraction:

$$\delta^V = (Z^V - h)/(Z - Z^V) \tag{5}$$

The larger the atom, the smaller the value of the valence delta. As a result, the valence delta value is a direct count of valence electrons, weighted by the number of core electrons.

If the algorithm above is used, then the δ^V values for the second quantum level atoms in Table 1 would be halved since $Z - Z^V = 2$ for this level. A more satisfactory denominator is $Z - Z^V - 1$. This preserves the original delta assignment logic and numerical values for the second quantum level atoms. This denominator can be justified in a logical way if the suppressed hydrogen atom is viewed as the zero-valued reference structure in counting non-valence electrons. To normalize all $Z - Z^V$ to a zero electron count for hydrogen, one must be subtracted. The final equation for all heteroatoms then becomes:

$$\delta^V = (Z^V - h)/(Z - Z^V - 1) \tag{6}$$

Numerical values for several higher level atoms are shown in Table 2.

TABLE 2.   Valence delta values for neutral 3rd quantum
level atoms and halogens.

Atom	Z^V-h	$Z-Z^V-1$	δ^V
P	3	9	0.33
	4	9	0.44
	5	9	0.56
S	5	9	0.56
	6	9	0.67
Cl	7	9	0.78
Br	7	27	0.26
I	7	47	0.16

F.   Heteroatoms in Higher Oxidation States

The sulfur and phosphorus atoms in Table 2 are found in molecules
in their lowest oxidation states.   These atoms can expand their
valences through coordinate covalent bonding with atoms such as
oxygen.   This gives rise to sulfites, sulfates and phosphates which
are of interest in biological QSAR studies.

It is not readily apparent how the general expression for δ^V,
described above, can be used for sulfur and phosphorus in these
oxygenated groups.   Vogel (1948) has observed from the deduction
of fragment contributions to molar refractivities, that S, SO and SO_2
make virtually identical contributions.   This implies that the size of
the central sulfur atom decreases with successive oxygen bonding.
The trend of δ^V_S values reflecting this must be to increase with
increasing oxygen bonding in the group if it is assumed that δ^V_O is
constant through the series.

TABLE 3.   Valence delta values for sulfur and phosphorus in higher
            oxidation states.

Atom	δ^V Fraction	δ^V Number
S in –S–S–	8/9	0.89
S in –SO–	12/9	1.33
S in –SO$_2$–	24/9	2.67
P in –$\overset{\shortmid}{P}$O–	20/9	2.22

At this time it is not possible to derive δ^V for these cases from
the logic presented; however, from molar refractivities for series of
compounds, it is possible to obtain empirical values of δ^V shown in
Table 3.   The fractional value of δ^V is included to illustrate
relationships within the series S, SO and SO$_2$ and P and PO.   This
could form the basis for further study and the ultimate theoretical
prediction of these δ^V values.

5. Summary

It is clear from the definitions used in deriving the various
indexes that specific molecular fragments are counted and encoded
into the values calculated.   Stated another way, the numerical value
of a particular index gives us information about molecular structure
in terms of the presence and number of molecular fragments of a
particular kind.   These indexes become the basis of relationships
between molecular structure and physical and biological properties of
molecules.

We have reviewed in this chapter all of the basic elements which make up the molecular connectivity method to date. Since writing the first book on this subject in 1976, we have made several advances in the molecular connectivity method, permitting us to conduct calculations on heteroatom-containing molecules, heretofore not possible. The real advances, however, have come in our understanding of the significance of the indexes and particularly the delta values. By probing for the physical significance of the delta values, we have carried the molecular connectivity paradigm beyond just a topological description into the realm of electronic and orbital structure description. Chapters 3 and 4 will elaborate on these advances.

Examples of Calculations

Calculations of molecular connectivity indexes are extremely simple. The only input is the connection pattern and the atom identities. The molecules are then dissected into the appropriate paths or fragments and the algorithm applied. A few examples follow to illustrate these calculations. Although the calculations are very simple, it is clear that a computer is very fast and error free. Also, calculated indexes can be stored and manipulated in QSAR studies. This is strongly recommended.

1. Ethyl Acetate – $^1\chi^V$

    a. δ^V assignment

    b. first order
        bond dissection $(1\cdot2),(2\cdot6),(6\cdot4),(4\cdot6),(4\cdot1)$

    c. summation
        of bond terms $^1\chi = 0.707 + 0.289 + 0.204 +$
        $0.204 + 0.500$
        $^1\chi^V = 1.904$

2. <u>p - Xylene</u> - $^4X_{pc}$

a. δ assignment

b. dissection into
   path/cluster
   fragments

c. summation
   of bond terms

$$^4X_{pc} = 4(1 \cdot 3 \cdot 2 \cdot 2 \cdot 2)^{-0.5}$$

$$^4X_{pc} = 1.156$$

3. <u>Trifluoroacetic Acid</u> - $^3X_p^v$

a. δ^v assignment

b. dissection into
   3-path fragments

   3(F–C–C=O)

   3(F–C–C–OH)

c. summation of
   fragment terms

$$^3X_p^v = 3(7 \cdot 4 \cdot 4 \cdot 6)^{-0.5} + 3(7 \cdot 4 \cdot 4 \cdot 5)^{-0.5}$$

$$^3X_p^v = 0.243$$

References

Allen, T. L. (1959). Bond energies and the interactions between next-nearest neighbors. I. Saturated hydrocarbons, diamond, sulfanes and organic sulfur compounds. J. Chem. Phys. 31, 1039-1049.

Amidon, G. L. and Anik, S. T. (1976). Comparison of several molecular topological indexes with molecular surface area in aqueous solubility estimation. J. Pharm. Sci. 65, 801-806.

Bawden, D. (1983). Computerized chemical structure-handling techniques in structure-activity studies and molecular property prediction. J. Chem. Inf. Comput. Sci., 23, 14-22.

Fajans, K. (1920). The energy of the atomic unions in the diamond and in aliphatic hydrocarbons. Chem. Ber. 53, 643-665.

Franklin, J. F. (1949). Prediction of heat and free energies of organic compounds. Ind. Eng. Chem. 41, 1070-1076.

Kier, L. B., Hall, L. H., Murray, W. J. and Randic, M. (1975). Molecular connectivity I: Relationship to nonspecific local anesthesia. J. Pharm. Sci., 64, 1971-1974.

Kier, L. B. and Hall, L. H. (1976). Molecular connectivity VII: Specific treatment of heteroatoms. J. Pharm. Sci. 65, 1806-1809.

Kier, L. B., Hall, L. H., Murray, W. J. and Randic, M. (1976). Molecular connectivity V: Connectivity series applied to density. J. Pharm. Sci., 65, 1226-1230.

Klages, F. (1949). An improvement in the additive calculation of heats of combustion and the calculation of mesomerism energy from heats of combustion. Chem. Ber. 49, 358-375.

Laidler, K. J. (1956). A system of molecular thermochemistry for organic gases and liquids. Can. J. Chem. 34, 626-648.

Pauling, L. (1960). The Nature of the Chemical Bond. Cornell Univ. Press, Ithaca, N.Y. Chapt. 3.

Randic, M. (1975). On characterization of molecular branching. J. Am. Chem. Soc. 97, 6609-6615.

Somayajulu, G. R. and Zwolinski, B. J. (1966). Generalized treatment of alkanes. Trans. Faraday Soc. 62, 2327-2340.

Vogel, A. I. (1948). Physical properties and chemical constitution. XXIII. Investigation of the so-called coordinate link in esters of oxy-acids and intro-paraffins by molar refractivity determinations. J. Chem. Soc. 1833-1855.

CHAPTER 2
Relation to
Physical Properties

An objective in developing the molecular connectivity method is to provide a general procedure for establishing relationships between molecular structure and various physicochemical properties. The ability to estimate property values has become increasingly important, whether they are basically physicochemical or complex biological activities. In this chapter we explore relationships between structure, represented by molecular connectivity indexes, and physical properties. These properties were selected as a test of the structural information because the quality of such data is generally superior to that of biological measurements.

The principal objective of this chapter is to show that models of physical properties based on chi indexes are well established in the statistical sense. Relations based on connectivity indexes can show very close agreement to accurate physical data. Such sound relations provide confidence in the structure-based approach of molecular connectivity, especially because of the wide variety of properties illustrated. As a result, any notion of a "mere statistical basis" for connectivity relations seems most unlikely.

Yet, there is an additional reason for the material in this chapter. The high quality statistical relations developed herein can be used as a basis for property estimations. Indeed, some investigators have been approaching molecular connectivity for just such purposes. In Chapter 8, the section on chromatography indicates the significant amount of work being done in this area. Although we do not necessarily state that the equations presented in this chapter are entirely appropriate for prediction, we do believe that work such as presented here can be the basis for useful property estimation. For this reason, use of molecular connectivity in data base approaches is an especially attractive method for QSAR.

In Chapter 1 we showed that the different chi indexes vary with changes in molecular structure. For open chain molecules, the $^1\chi$ index systematically decreases as the skeleton becomes more branched. Also, $^2\chi$ increases with increased branching. These two indexes convey different information about the degree of branching, as shown by the modest correlation between the two indexes. We will show by example that this parallel to skeletal branching also varies with property values. In Chapter 1 we showed that the presence of heteroatoms is encoded in the valence delta values and in the chi valence indexes. In this chapter we examine property dependence on atom type and structural position using correlations with chi indexes.

1. Molar Refraction

Among the best physical data available and of interest for estimation, especially in biological studies, is molar refraction. The ACS Advances in Chemistry Series provides a ready source of tabulated data. (Dreisbach, 1955, 1959, 1961).

A. Alkanes

It is of theoretical interest to test methods on data for alkanes because good data are generally available for complete isomer sets. This is the case for alkane molar refraction. Data are available for liquid alkanes from pentanes through octanes plus many nonanes, making a total of 55 values. All but 14 of the nonanes have five significant figure data. Molar refraction values range from 25 to 45 (Dreisbach, 1959).

No single variable equation gives a correlation with a standard deviation, s, better than 0.2, including ^1X and the count of carbon atoms. However, ^1X and ^2X together drop the s to 0.13 and the addition of ^0X reduces the standard error to 0.06. Addition of variables continues to decrease the error towards 0.02 for six variables. In the present analysis we quote the relationship for four variables. In light of the number of data points and the possibility of chance correlations, experience suggests that four variables constitute a very reasonable equation:

$$MR = 3.832\,^0X + 4.438\,^1X - 0.8727\,^3X_p - 0.4828\,^4X_p - 0.4558$$
$$r = 0.99999, \quad s = 0.043, \quad F = 194694, \quad n = 55$$

The residual for only one compound (2,3,5-trimethylhexane) exceeds two standard deviations (0.102). The molar refraction for this compound is known only to four significant figures.

The two variables ^0X and ^1X carry similar information relating to the number of carbon atoms and to skeletal branching. The other two, ^3X_p and ^4X_p, encode information on the details of molecular structure. Except for the ^0X and ^1X indexes, these variables are not highly intercorrelated.

B. Alkyl Benzenes

A smaller set of excellent data is available for alkyl substituted benzenes containing six to ten carbon atoms. It is of interest to investigate the use of chi indexes for aromatic molecules. This data set includes benzene and all polymethyl and polyethyl substituted derivatives for which there is quality data (Dreisbach, 1955).

The number of carbon atoms gives a correlation with s = 0.14, but this is not helpful in combination with other indexes to produce an improved correlation. Three chi indexes yield a relationship with a standard error of 0.018. For this data set of 24 compounds, the two variable equation is:

$$MR = 7.004 \, {}^{1}X^{V} + 4.027 \, {}^{2}X^{V} + 7.548$$
$$r = 0.99999, \ s = 0.047, \ F = 141550, \ n = 24$$

There are no compounds with residuals greater than two standard deviations.

C. Polarizability of a Mixed Data Set

Molecular polarizability is directly proportional to molar refraction and has been used as a correlation variable in QSAR studies. A particularly interesting data set was developed by Agin et al (1965) for use in a study of local anesthetic potency. This set of 36 compounds includes methanol, acetone, ethyl ether, phenol, benzimidazole, ephedrine, tetracaine, quinine and other molecules of varied structure. The data are not nearly of the quality of the previous sets but, nonetheless, represent a challenge to estimate within 1 to 2 units.

A single variable, either ${}^{1}X$ or the number of skeletal atoms, yields a standard error of 2.3. The two variables ${}^{O}X$ and ${}^{1}X$, however, drop the standard error to 1.85.

$$P = 5.49 \, {}^{1}X + 2.36 \, {}^{O}X + 0.864$$
$$r = 0.998, \ s = 1.85, \ F = 3301, \ n = 36$$

The fact that valence indexes do not significantly decrease the standard error strongly suggests that for this data set polarizability does not depend heavily on atom type, within the error limits of the data. The variation in skeletal arrangement, including number of rings, is adequately described by ${}^{O}X$ and ${}^{1}X$. These studies show that molecular connectivity can be used to establish good quantitative relations between structure and molar refraction.

2. Water Solubility

The processes associated with solubility are many and complex. It is clear that water solubility appears to vary systematically with molecular structure in such a way that structure-property relationships can be developed. Two examples illustrate the potential for analysis of solubility in closely related series of compounds.

A. Alcohols

In an early paper published on the molecular connectivity method (Hall et al, 1975), good correlations were shown between the ^1X index and solubility. For a set of 51 aliphatic alcohols, ^1X yielded a correlation coefficient of 0.978 with standard error of 0.36. The position of the -OH moiety in the skeleton influences solubility. This factor was included explicitly by using as a variable the ^1X term for the C-OH bond (C_{OH} in the paper). This improved the correlation to r = 0.991, s = 0.29. Some of the 51 compounds have solubilities which are less reliable and for that reason we include only 38 compounds to obtain the following two-variable equation:

$$-\log[\text{solubility}] = 11.267\,^1X - 8.643\,^1X^V - 9.417$$
$$r = 0.995, \ s = 0.23, \ n = 38$$

Adding additional chi indexes can reduce the standard error to 0.19 for four variables; however, the two-variable equation produces an adequate standard error for estimation purposes.

B. Halobenzenes

Yalkowsky et al (1979) have produced a set of excellent data for halogen substituted benzenes. The 35 compounds include all four halogens as substituents and a few compounds with more than one halogen. In their paper Yalkowsky has shown the importance of melting point as a factor in understanding water solubility, especially in a data set with both liquids and solids and where the melting point varies significantly. In this present data set, 17 compounds are liquids while the melting points vary from 27 to 230°C among the solids.

Two connectivity variables in addition to the melting point give excellent results.

$$-\log[\text{solubility}] = 0.890\,{}^1X + 0.627\,{}^2X^v + 0.00979\,mp - 2.004$$
$$r = 0.995,\ s = 0.15,\ F = 951,\ n = 35$$

In this analysis there is only one residual greater than two standard deviations, 1,3-diiodobenzene. It is interesting to note that this is also the only compound with a large residual found in Yalkowsky's correlation with melting point, calculated surface area or estimated partition coefficient. The fluorine-containing molecules are all well fitted, as is benzene. The intercorrelation of ${}^1X$ and ${}^2X^v$ is very small, $r^2 = 0.26$, indicating that these two variables encode rather different information. The ${}^1X$ index is independent of atom type and represents general skeletal variation. The ${}^2X^v$ index, on the other hand, depends heavily on atom type, especially for halogens. Further, ${}^2X^v$ is more sensitive to skeletal variation than is ${}^1X$.

The coefficient of the melting point is very nearly 0.01 as suggested by the theoretical development of Yalkowsky. It is concluded then that chi indexes are very useful in the relation between structure and the water solubility of halogen-substituted benzenes.

3. Molar Volume

Considerations of molecular bulk are very important in a number of research areas. Various measures of size contribute to the notion of molecular bulk. In experimental terms the best defined aspect of bulk is the molecular volume, which can be determined from density determinations.

J. T. Edward and coworkers (1978) (1979) have published excellent sets of data in which the value of the molar volume, V^o, is determined by least squares extrapolation of the apparent molal volume to infinite dilution in carbon tetrachloride solution. From accurate and precise density measurements, data are available with four significant figures.

A. Alkanes

For alkanes, data are available for pentanes up to decanes from Edward (1978). In addition, six values are available from Longworth (1966) extending the compounds up to dotriacontane with the data ranging from 116.2 ml to 565.8 ml.

Three connectivity variables give a good account of the molar volume:

$$V^o = 24.87\,^1X + 11.86\,^2X - 2.844\,^4X_{pc} + 39.79$$
$$r = 0.9999, \ s = 1.17, \ F = 86615, \ n = 37.$$

Addition of other terms decreases the standard error below 1 ml. For our purposes an estimated error around 1 ml is quite good, representing a relative error less than 1%. The three chi indexes are not highly intercorrelated and carry different information about structure. ^1X is dependent on the number of atoms as well as skeletal branching; ^2X is highly sensitive to skeletal branching, and $^4X_{pc}$ encodes specific structural aspects associated with gem and vic substitution. The negative sign of $^4X_{pc}$ probably reflects the volume decrease due to structural accommodation for sterically crowded structures.

B. Quarternary Ammonium Salts

Using methods similar to those of Edward (1978), Barlow (1971) has determined the apparent molar volumes of a series of quaternary ammonium salts in dilute aqueous solution. The substituents on nitrogen include methyl and ethyl, as well as various cyclic groups including the nitrogen and four or five carbon atoms.

In this study the nitrogen atom is a relatively constant feature; hence, no valence chi indexes are required. A two-variable equation is:

$$V^o = 22.15 \, {}^oX - 2.019 \, {}^4X_{pc} + 27.70$$
$$r = 0.999, \ s = 1.23, \ F = 3185, \ n = 18.$$

There are no residuals greater than two standard deviations. The regression standard error represents a relative error of less than 1%.

4. Chromatographic Retention Data

An area of considerable interest for structure-property relations is the use of retention indexes from gas chromatography. Several investigators have approached the problem from various points of view. The ability to estimate the retention index for a given compound from its structure appears to be very useful. The ease of calculation of chi indexes makes their use very attractive in this field.

A. Alkanes

Millership and Woolfson (1977) have developed good data on 18 alkanes. The compounds range in size from ethane to 2,2,4-trimethyl pentane.

The two chi indexes ${}^1X$ and ${}^3X_p$ produce a very good relationship:

$$RI = 0.719 \, {}^1X + 0.125 \, {}^3X_p - 0.242$$
$$r = 0.998, \ s = 0.045, \ F = 1702, \ n = 18$$

Only ethane has a residual twice the standard deviation. The branched compounds are predicted as accurately as the straight chain compounds.

B. Polyaromatic Hydrocarbons

Another class of molecules illustrating the utility of molecular connectivity is the polyaromatic hydrocarbons. Lee, White et al (1979) have provided excellent gas chromatographic data from SE-52 capillary columns. We have selected 32 compounds containing six-membered rings, up to six in number. The retention indexes range from 200 for naphthalene up to 503.9 for dibenzo[def,mno]-chrysene.

The single index, ^1X, yields a correlation coefficient $r = 0.998$ with a standard deviation of $s = 5.8$. The addition of the chain-6 index, $^6X_{ch}$, lowers the standard deviation to 4.5. The following three-variable equation shows excellent statistics:

$$RI = 35.0 \, ^0X^V + 100.0 \, ^6X_{ch} + 9.20 \, ^4X_p - 38.0$$
$$r = 0.999, \; s = 3.85, \; F = 5021, \; n = 32.$$

Additional indexes decrease the standard error still further, but these three variables indicate the potential quality of the analysis. The $^0X^V$ relates strongly to the atom count, modified by the bonding environment. The $^6X_{ch}$ index varies with the type of embedded six-membered ring.

C. Pyrazine Carbothioamides

Kaliszan and Foks (1977) showed that the simple connectivity index, ^1X, can be used to relate to the R_M values for reversed-phase thin layer chromatographic data. The data set consists of 20 ring substituted pyrazine carbothioamides. The substituents consist of oxygen and nitrogen-containing groups from two to eleven atoms. For the 20 molecules, an equation was found:

$$R_M = 0.733 \, ^1X - 0.225 \qquad r = 0.946$$

The ^1X index was calculated for the substituent group only. This is a useful technique when a portion of the structure is constant throughout the series.

Kaliszan and Foks did not make use of the valence delta values in their analysis. A later study revealed significant improvement when valence indexes are introduced. The $^0X^V$ index alone gives $r = 0.961$, $s = 0.23$, $F = 215$. The use of two variables is better.

$$R_M = 0.402\,^1X + 1.827\,^3X^V_c - 1.994$$
$$r = 0.973, \quad s = 0.19, \quad F = 148, \quad n = 20$$

There are no residuals greater than twice the standard error. Compounds with aromatic and nonaromatic substituent groups are fitted equally well to the regression equation.

D. Aliphatic Alcohols

An excellent set of gas chromatographic data has been provided by Spivakovskii et al (1977). The authors also propose a method for selecting structural groups based on types of bonds. Unfortunately, their additive scheme uses 14 variables for the 32 alcohols in the data set. The connectivity indexes may be used to form a much more economical model, and yet possess outstanding statistical qualities.

The two first order indexes give a good correlation:

$$RI = 486\,^1X - 293\,^1X^V + 44.9 \qquad r = 0.995, \quad s = 10.1$$

The addition of the ^2X and $^4X^V_p$ decreases the standard error to 8.4. The addition of the $^2X^V$ and $^5X^V_p$ indexes drops the standard error to the level achieved by Spivakovskii et al; however, only 6 chi indexes are required compared to the 14 substructural fragments used by Spivakovskii.

$$RI = 1010\,^1X - 770.9\,^1X^V + 123.2\,^2X - 136.7\,^2X^V - 37.98\,^4X_p$$
$$- 62.47\,^5X_p^V - 261.1$$
$$r = 0.999, \quad s = 5.78, \quad F = 1647, \quad n = 32$$

No residual exceeds two standard deviations. The data set includes pentanols through nonanols in various isomeric forms, including primary, secondary and tertiary alcohols. It should be pointed out that the use of 14 variables by Spivakovskii makes the number of degrees of freedom unacceptably low for 32 observations. We have frequently found that connectivity-based regression models are statistically quite economical.

5. Thermodynamic Properties

Some of the best experimental data is based on accurate calorimetric information. Heat of formation, ΔH_f, and heat of vaporization, ΔH_v, are available for a wide variety of structures. A small number of examples are recorded for illustration.

A. Heat of Atomization

In the first book on the molecular connectivity method, Kier and Hall (1976) discussed results for alkanes in some detail. In this work we present only results for alcohols, ethers and thiols. It should be pointed out that ΔH_a depends on atom count n so heavily that this variable is introduced directly into the regression equation. All of these compounds have one heteroatom:

Alcohols: $\quad \Delta H_a = 279.99n + 22.28\,\Delta X - 69.97$
$$r = 0.9999, \quad s = 1.01, \quad n = 19$$

Ethers: $\quad \Delta H_a = 281.05n + 13.03\,\Delta X - 83.03$
$$r = 0.9999, \quad s = 2.37, \quad n = 12$$

Thiols: $\quad \Delta H_a = 280.08n + 12.66\,\Delta X - 109.25$
$$r = 0.9999, \quad s = 0.30, \quad n = 14$$

The variable ΔX is the value of the difference in ^1X between a branched isomer and the normal isomer:

$$\Delta X = {}^1X(\text{n-isomer}) - {}^1X(\text{branched isomer})$$

This type of "difference" chi index is often useful when there is a heavy dependence on the number of atoms or when the property value increases with n and increases with skeletal branching. The value of ^1X increases with homologation but decreases with branching.

B. Heat of Vaporization - ΔH_v

An important property related to intermolecular forces is the heat of vaporization. A set of 20 alcohols is available for study. Again, there is significant dependence on the number of carbon atoms.

$$\Delta H_v = 1.163n - 4.083\Delta X + 6.641$$
$$r = 0.993, \ s = 0.36, \ n = 20$$

When the corresponding equation for alkanes is given, a useful structural interpretation is obtained.

$$\Delta H_v = 1.191n - 2.384 \ \Delta X + 0.282$$
$$r = 0.998, \ s = 0.16, \ n = 44$$

The coefficient of n is essentially the same for both, suggesting that the alkyl contribution is about the same. On the other hand, the constant term is about 6 kcal larger for alcohols, reflecting the average strength of the hydrogen bonding in alcohols. Further, the coefficient of the skeletal branching term, ΔX, is significantly larger for alcohols, suggesting that the position of the -OH group is quite important in understanding the magnitude of ΔH_v. The skeletal branching can, in fact, be partitioned between branching due to alkyl skeletal effects and branching arising from -OH group position. Contributions due to the -OH position are significantly greater than those due to $-CH_3$ group positions. When analyzed this way, details of structural influence on properties can be developed for use.

From the point of view of structure, ΔH is perhaps not the most appropriate quantity for structure correlation. Enthalpy is a compound quantity, made up of internal energy U and the pressure-volume product PV:

$$H = U + PV$$

For vaporization it can be shown that $\Delta U_{vap} = \Delta H_{vap} - RT_b$ where T_b is the normal boiling point. The internal energy is more directly related to structure than enthalpy. For this reason we have examined a large set of alkanes with chi indexes to find a relation to internal energy. In general, somewhat higher quality correlations are found for ΔU than ΔH.

From the ACS Advances in Chemistry Series, Dreisbach (1959), we obtained a set of 74 compounds with high quality data. With only three chi indexes, an excellent relationship is observed:

$$\Delta U = 2.387 \, {}^1X - 0.2477 \, {}^4X_p - 0.1895 \, {}^5X_p^v - 0.0691$$
$$r = 0.998, \ s = 0.088, \ F = 7421, \ n = 74$$

This is an excellent correlation and can be improved even further with the addition of other connectivity indexes.

6. Other Properties

A. Magnetic Susceptibility

Diamagnetic substances are repelled by a homogeneous magnetic field. The proportionality constant k between the field strength and the sample magnetization is known as the magnetic susceptibility. The molar magnetic susceptibility, X_M, is given as

$$X_M = kM/d$$

where M is the molecular weight and d is the density. As a molar property, the susceptibility may be correlated with structural indexes. For a data set of 18 alcohols (Hall and Kier, 1976), two indexes give an excellent correlation.

$$X_M = 51.56\,^1X^v - 29.71\,^1X + 25.74$$
$$r = 0.995, \ s = 2.3, \ n = 18$$

The use of the $^3X_p^v$ index in conjunction with $^1X^v$ gives an even better correlation:

$$X_M = 22.8\,^1X^v + 7.62\,^3X_p^v + 10.90$$
$$r = 0.999, \ s = 0.90, \ n = 18$$

This standard error represents a relative error of about 1%.

B. Van der Waals Equation Constants

The two constants in the van der Waals equation have been used as parameters in various models. Since these constants have not been measured for a large number of molecules, it would be helpful to have a simple method to estimate the a and b parameters.

Kier and Hall (1976) analysed a set of 20 molecules including acetone, chloroform, ethylamine, diethylsulfide, propyl alcohol and proprionitrile. The simple chi index gives a good correlation with the a value while ^1X and $^1X^v$ correlate well with the b value.

For this present work a larger set of van der Waals constants has been analyzed. This set of 73 compounds includes such molecules as acetone, acetylene, aniline, chloroform, ethylamine, ethyl chloride, diethylsulfide, fluorobenzene, methanol, xylenes, isobutylformate, ethyl ether, ethylene dichloride, iodobenzene, naphthalene, thiophene, and trimethylamine.

For both the a and b constants, a single chi index yields statistically significant results with F values around 1000. Results using three indexes will be given here.

$$a = -2.134\,{}^{o}X + 3.265\,{}^{o}X^{V} + 7.508\,{}^{1}X - 2.899$$
$$r = 0.984, \quad s = 1.67, \quad F = 709, \quad n = 73$$

$$b = 0.01426\,{}^{o}X + 0.01753\,{}^{o}X^{V} - 0.01100\,{}^{3}X_{c} + 0.00085$$
$$r = 0.984, \quad s = 0.008, \quad F = 702, \quad n = 73$$

The residuals show no trends and, for the a constant, only three residuals are greater than twice the standard error; for the b constant, only two residuals exceed twice the standard error.

An alternative relation of chi indexes may be used for explicit relation to molecular volume or volume-dependent properties. It has been shown (Hall and Kier, 1981) that the delta values relate to van der Waals volume. In Chapter 3 there is a discussion of the relation of the delta values to the van der Waals volume of molecules. A linear combination of a simple chi index and its valence counterpart may be used as follows:

$$sum_{0} = {}^{o}X + {}^{o}X^{V} \quad \text{and} \quad diff_{0} = {}^{o}X - {}^{o}X^{V}$$

$$sum_{1} = {}^{1}X + {}^{1}X^{V} \quad \text{and} \quad diff_{1} = {}^{1}X - {}^{1}X^{V}$$

$$sum_{2} = {}^{2}X + {}^{2}X^{V} \quad \text{and} \quad diff_{2} = {}^{2}X - {}^{2}X^{V}$$

The van der Waals constants have been investigated with these sum and difference variables. Results using a single sum/difference variable are as follows:

$$a = 4.854\,sum_{1} - 2.581 \qquad r = 0.980, \quad s = 1.87, \quad F = 1688, \quad n = 73$$
$$b = 0.02277\,sum_{1} + 0.0242 \qquad r = 0.971, \quad s = 0.0105, \quad F = 1185, \quad n = 73$$

These results indicate a higher level of statistical significance than was obtained with a single chi index.

Using two of these sum/difference variables, improved statistics are obtained.

$$a = 4.698 sum_1 + 1.131 diff_1 - 2.490$$
$$r = 0.981, \quad s = 1.80, \quad F = 916, \quad n = 73$$

$$b = 0.01049 sum_0 + 0.007270 sum_1 + 0.0086$$
$$r = 0.984, \quad s = 0.0079, \quad F = 1061, \quad n = 73$$

The difference variable ($diff_1 = {}^1X - {}^1X^V$) contributes to the a constant. The $diff_1$ variable is related to the electronic properties of the molecule. The b constant is related only to the sum variable which expresses the volume of the molecule. This is to be expected since the b constant is dependent on the molecular volume. On the other hand, the diff variables relate to the electronic structure of the molecules. Since the a constant represents the intermolecular forces, it is not surprising that the $diff_1$ variable should be important in the equation for the a constant. Use is made of these volume dependent variables in Chapter 6, section 6B.

7. Summary

In this chapter we have examined data for a variety of properties and molecular structures. Correlations of high quality have been demonstrated for a reasonable number of connectivity indexes. It appears that regression models can be developed for a variety of properties. We refer the reader to Chapter 8 and its list of literature references which represent a wide range of QSAR studies.

References

Agin, D., Hersch, L. and Holtzman, D. (1965). The action of anesthetics on excitable membranes: A quantum chemical analysis. Proc. Nat. Acad. Sci., 53, 952-958.

Barlow, R. B., Lowe, B. M., Pearson, J. D. M., Rendall, H. M. and Thompson, G. M. (1971). Ion size and activity at acetylcholine receptors. Molec. Pharmacol., 7, 357-366.

Driesbach, R. R. (1955). Physical Properties of Chemical Compounds, Advances in Chemistry Series, Number 15. American Chemical Society.

Driesbach, R. R. (1959). Physical Properties of Chemical Compounds, Advances in Chemistry Series, Number 22. American Chemical Society.

Driesbach, R. R. (1961). Physical Properties of Chemical Compounds, Advances in Chemistry Series, Number 29. American Chemical Society.

Edward, J. T., Farrell, P. G. and Shahidi, F. (1978). Partial molal volumes of organic compounds in carbon tetrachloride. 1. alkanes. conformational effects. J. Phys. Chem., 82, 2310-2313.

Edward, J. F., Farrell, P. G. and Shahidi, F. (1979). Partial molal volumes of organic compounds in carbon tetrachloride IV. Ketones, alcohols and ethers. Can. J. Chem., 57, 2585-2592.

Hall, L. H. and Kier, L. B. (1981). The relation of molecular connectivity to molecular volume and biological activity. Eur. J. Med. Chem., 16, 399-407.

Hall, L. H., Kier, L. B. and Murray, W. J. (1975). Molecular connectivity II. Relationship to water solubility and boiling point. J. Pharm. Sci., 64, 1974-1977.

Kaliszan, K. and Foks, H. (1977). The relationship between the Rm values and the connectivity indices for pyrazine carbothioamide derivatives. Chromatographia, 10, 346-349.

Kier, L. B. and Hall, L. H. (1976). Molecular Connectivity in Chemistry and Drug Research. Academic Press, New York.

Lee, M. L., Vassilaros, D. L., White, C. M. and Novotny, M. (1979). Retention indices for programmed temperature capillary-column gas chromatography of polycyclic aromatic hydrocarbons. Anal. Chem., 51, 768-774.

Longworth, L. G. (1966). Diffusion of hydrogen-bonding solutes in carbon tetrachloride. J. Colloid Interface Sci., 22, 3-11.

Millership, J. S. and Woolfson, A. D. (1977). Correlation of gas chromatographic retention parameters with molecular connectivity. J. Pharm. Pharmacol., 29, 75-79.

Spivakovskii, G. I., Tishchenko, A. I., Zaslovskii, I. I. and Wulfson, N. S. (1977). Calculation of retention indices of compounds from their structural formulae for combined identification by gas chromatography-mass spectrometry. J. Chromo., 144, 1-16.

Yalkowsky, S. H., Orr, R. J. and Valvani, S. C. (1979). Solubility and Partitioning 3. The solubility of halobenzenes in water. Ind. Eng. Chem., 18, 351-353.

CHAPTER 3

Topological Information

1. Information from ^1X and $^1X^v$

A. Relative Degree of Branching

The original algorithm was designed to rank alkanes according to the inexact notion of branching (Randic, 1975). In Table 1 are listed the nine isomers of heptane, ranked according to the decreasing value of the ^1X index. A categorical breakdown of the four possible delta values for each isomer follows the index value. An inspection of the list of isomers satisfies our intuition that the molecules may be increasingly branched as we go down the list. There is no way to verify quantitatively this intuition, although we would suspect that increased branching should influence certain geometrical char- acteristics such as volume and surface area. These geometrical properties are inexact since an atom (hence, a molecule) has no precise boundaries, but has contours of decreasing probability of electron occupancy. These characteristics will be covered later in this section.

An inspection of Table 1 reveals that an increase in branching in a molecule results in an increase in the number of atom δ values larger than 2. Each occurrence of a $(\delta_i \delta_j)^{-0.5}$ term in computing ^1X in which a $\delta_i = 3$ or $\delta_i = 4$ value appears leads to a smaller numerical value for that term compared to a $(1 \cdot \delta_j)^{-0.5}$ or a $(2 \cdot \delta_j)^{-0.5}$ term. Each atom with a $\delta_i = 3$ requires the presence of three $(3 \cdot \delta_j)^{-0.5}$ terms associated with that atom, while each atom with $\delta_i = 4$ requires the presence of four $(4 \cdot \delta_j)^{-0.5}$ terms associated with that atom. Thus, the influence of larger values at branched atoms, combined with more product terms with at least one large value, leads to a summation (^1X value) that is lower, coincident with branching.

B. Molecular Size

The size of a molecule, expressed as the number of non-hydrogen atoms, is encoded in the ^1X index. In an homologous series of alkanes the structural increment is $-CH_2-$. Each higher homolog, therefore, adds a $(2 \cdot 2)^{-0.5}$ term or 0.500 to the value of ^1X. The contribution of a $-CH_2-CH_3$ bond to molecular size is clearly greater than that of a $C-CH$. This relation is given by the corresponding bond term sizes: $(2 \cdot 1)^{-0.5}$ viz $(4 \cdot 3)^{-0.5}$. This size contribution is correctly given by the bond term formula, $(\delta_i \delta_j)^{-0.5}$.

C. Molecular Volume

From Table 1 it is apparent that increased branching must influence the shape and global volume of a molecule. Although molecular volume is an inexact attribute because of the indeterminate positions of electrons, approximations can be used in calculating a theoretical volume of a molecule with a certain probability. The most common approach is to use the van der Waals radii of atoms to define a surface from which a volume and a surface area can be computed. This radius is a function of the probability contour of electrons in valence orbitals. Calculations of volume are thus fairly consistent from one atom to the next. The calculation of molecular volume from these atomic radii is more complex since atomic orbitals overlap to varying degrees in bond formation and across space in a molecular structure. Estimates of this overlap and orbital size contraction vary according to the method. The estimation of molecular volumes is thus not a highly refined procedure.

TABLE 1.   Delta values of atoms in heptane isomers.

| Heptane | $^1\chi$ | Counts of δ Values | | | |
		1	2	3	4
	3.414	2	5	0	0
	3.346	3	3	1	0
	3.308	3	3	1	0
	3.270	3	3	1	0
	3.181	4	1	2	0
	3.126	4	1	2	0
	3.121	4	2	0	1
	3.061	4	2	0	1
	2.943	5	0	1	1

One estimate of atomic, group and molecular volume from van der Waals radii is due to Bondi (1964). A critical test of the volume information content encoded in molecular connectivity indexes is to examine the atom and group volume estimates of Bondi and to attempt to relate these to the connectivity delta values describing these atoms or groups. From an assessment of electron orbital contributions, the volume of an atom bound to other atoms should be a consequence of valence electrons in sigma, σ , pi, p, and lone pair orbitals, n. The volume of a sigma orbital is due to the presence of two electrons, although only one such electron is contributed by an atom under consideration. We can expect that an atom volume should be some function:

$$V = f \ (2\sigma + p + n) \tag{1}$$

Kier and Hall (1981) have found that this count of electrons does indeed correlate highly with Bondi atom and group calculated volumes. See Table 2 for this relationship. This expression can be stated in terms of molecular connectivity delta values:

$$V = (\sigma + p + n-h) + (\sigma - h) = \quad \delta^v + \delta \tag{2}$$

where h is a count of σ electrons bound to hydrogen.

The valence delta, δ^v, is a count of all (non-hydrogen) valence electrons, and the simple delta, δ , is a count of all adjacent (non-hydrogen) atoms; hence, δ is a count of only sigma electrons. An equation relating the connectivity delta values to the Bondi volumes and statistics is:

$$V \ (Bondi) = 17.03 - 1.59 \ (\delta^v + \delta) \tag{3}$$
$$r = 0.990, \ s = 0.52, \ n = 20, \ F = 859$$

The calculated values are shown in Table 2.

TABLE 2.   Delta values of valence-state atoms or hydrides and
Bondi volumes.

Atom/Hydride	δ	δ^V	Volume cm^3/mole	
			Bondi	Calculated
$-CH_3$	1	1	13.67	13.85
$-CH_2-$	2	2	10.23	10.67
$-CH$	3	3	6.78	7.49
$>C<$	4	4	3.33	4.31
$=CH_2$	1	2	11.94	12.26
$-C\equiv,\ =C=$	2	4	7.50	7.49
$\equiv CH$	1	3	11.55	10.67
$=CH-$	2	3	8.47	9.08
$-O-$	2	6	4.45	4.31
$-OH$	1	5	8.04	7.49
$-NH_2$	1	3	10.54	10.67
$-NH-$	2	4	8.08	7.49
$-N-$	3	5	4.33	4.31
$\equiv N$	1	5	7.90	7.49
$>C=$	3	4	5.54	5.90
$=O$	1	6	6.79	5.90
$=NH$	1	4	9.50	9.08
$=N-$	2	5	6.06	5.90
CH_4	0	0	17.12	17.03
NH_3	0	2	13.80	13.85

The ability of the atom delta values to correlate so well with these calculated volume values stimulates the belief that connectivity indexes such as ^1X and $^1X^V$ may correlate well with molecular volumes. For a molecule, recourse must be made to experimental estimates of volume such as partial molar volumes computed from density measurements. Several studies have explored the relationship between connectivity indexes and molecular volume. In one study, (Kier and Hall, 1981) the amino acid side chain volumes from partial molar volume experiments were found to correlate well with $^1X^V$, Table 3.

$$V \ (A^3) = 29.46\,^1X^V + 36.30 \tag{4}$$
$$r = 0.989, \ s = 3.93, \ n = 18, \ F = 696$$

Hall and Kier (1981) have found a very close correlation between the partial molar volume of 48 oxygenated compounds including 17 ethers, 13 ketones, 18 alcohols, and a multi-term connectivity equation. The equation and statistics are:

$$V = 32.58\,^0X^V - 12.51\,^0X + 4.867\,^1X^V - 3.184\,^4X_{pc} + 19.60 \tag{5}$$
$$r = 0.999, \ s = 1.51, \ F = 6543, \ n = 48$$

D. Molecular Surface Area

The molecular surface area, like molecular volume, can be estimated in several ways. Hermann (1972) has computed this attribute using van der Waals radii, taking a constant increment beyond the radius to approximate the surface of a cavity housing the molecule. The surface area can be approximated closely ($r = 0.987$) from the ^1X index, Table 4 (Kier, 1980a). A multi-term equation would undoubtedly improve this correlation significantly.

TABLE 3. Amino acid side chain volume and $^1\chi^v$.

Amino Acid	$^1\chi^v$	V (A^3)	V (A^3) calc.
Gly	0	36.3	36.3
Ala	0.577	52.6	53.3
Val	1.488	85.1	80.1
Leu	1.971	102.0	94.4
Ile	2.026	102.0	96.0
Phe	2.672	113.9	115.0
Pro	1.408	73.6	77.8
Trp	3.417	135.4	137.0
Tyr	2.807	116.2	119.0
His	2.079	91.1	97.6
Thr	1.169	71.2	70.7
Ser	0.724	54.9	57.6
Asn	1.255	72.4	73.3
Gln	1.755	92.7	88.0
Asp	1.190	68.4	71.4
Glu	1.690	84.7	86.1
Lys	2.224	105.1	101.8
Arg	2.550	109.1	111.4

E. Topology of Unsaturation and Heteroatoms

The valence delta value reflects the atom core charge, the numbers of pi and lone pair orbitals in addition to the non-hydrogen sigma bonds. Each of these structural features contributes to attributes such as atomic and molecular volume. In the case of unsaturated bonds, the contraction in bond length in the series $-CH_2-CH_2-$, $-CH=CH-$, and $-C\equiv C-$ is reflected in the decline of the bond index values of 0.500, 0.333 and 0.250, respectively; hence, a calculated volume from a molecular connectivity expression containing a $^{1}X^{V}$ term would parallel this trend. For heteroatoms in bonds, the δ^{V} values are inversely related to van der Waals radii, Table 5. The $^{0}X^{V}$ indexes calculated from these delta values correlate well with the van der Waals radii. The correlation coefficient is $r = 0.96$.

Another test of the topological information in δ^{V} values was a study of molar refraction, MR, values by Kier and Hall (1983a). The MR values of 101 mixed heteroatom molecules was equated with $^{1}X^{V}$, and an indicator variable counting hydrogens alpha to third quantum level heteroatoms. The list of structural types is shown in Table 6. The equation and statistics attest to the internal consistency of the δ^{V} values. It also reveals the relative volume information encoded in $^{1}X^{V}$ indexes.

$$MR = 9.042\,^{1}X^{V} - 1.286\ \alpha H + 4.777 \qquad (6)$$
$$r = 0.996, \ s = 1.038, \ n = 101, \ F = 6397$$

2. Information from ^{2}X and $^{2}X^{V}$

Experience has shown that for acyclic molecules, the ^{2}X index does not appear as a frequent descriptor of structure in regression analyses. In the case of alkane isomers, the ^{2}X values are inversely related to the ^{1}X indexes; hence, some of the same information is expected from both (Kier and Hall, 1976).

TABLE 4.   Cavity surface area and branching indexes.

Alkane	^1X	Computed Cavity Surface Area	Cavity Surface area from ^1X
Isobutane	1.732	249.1	247.0
Butane	1.914	255.2	257.5
Neopentane	2.000	270.1	262.0
2-Methylbutane	2.270	274.6	278.0
Pentane	2.414	287.0	286.3
2,2-Dimethylbutane	2.561	290.8	294.8
3-Methylpentane	2.807	300.0	309.0
Hexane	2.914	319.0	315.2
2,4-Dimethylpentane	3.125	324.7	327.3
Heptane	3.414	351.0	344.0

TABLE 5.   Van der Waals radii and $^oX^v$.

Atom with maximum no. of H.	δ^v	$^oX^v$	r_w (A)
F	7	0.378	1.40
O	5	0.447	1.42
N	3	0.577	1.46
C	1	1.000	1.53
Cl	0.78	1.132	1.75
S	0.67	1.222	1.80
P	0.33	1.733	1.86
Br	0.26	1.961	1.87
I	0.16	2.500	2.04

TABLE 6.   Molecules for MR calculation.

subset	number in subset
alkyl fluorides	9
alkyl chlorides	9
alkyl bromides	9
alkyl iodides	6
alkanols	6
dialkyl ethers	6
alkyl amines	6
alkyl nitriles	6
alkyl thiols	8
alkyl sulfides	9
alkyl phosphines	10
alkyl sulfites	4
alkyl sulfates	3
dialkyl disulfides	5
trialkyl orthophosphates	5
	101

The ^2X values among molecules in an isomeric series are calculated from differing numbers of $(\delta_i\ \delta_j\ \delta_k)^{-0.5}$ terms, depending upon the isomer. The magnitude of ^2X is, therefore, dependent not only on the values of δ_i, δ_j and δ_k in each fragment, but also on the number of fragments into which the molecule can be dissected. Only in the case of ^oX and ^1X (and the corresponding valence indexes) is the number of fragments the same for each molecule with the same number of atoms and bonds.

3. Information from the ^3X_p Index

A. Conformational Possibilities

The ^3X_p index is a weighted count of four atom (three-bond) fragments, of which the butane skeleton is the prototype. The calculation of the index is based on the algorithm $^3X_p = \Sigma \, (\delta_i \, \delta_j \, \delta_k \, \delta_l)^{-0.5}$, where the δ values reflect the degree of adjacency of each atom in the fragment. It is apparent that this structural fragment is the smallest unit in which the spatial relationship between the two terminal atoms is not entirely predictable. In the case of ^1X, ^2X and ^3X_c, the molecular fragments represented by these indexes are all well defined in space, based on standard bond lengths and angles. In the case of ^3X_p, the fragments represented have a potential for rotation around the central bond. This fragment, therefore, is the smallest molecular structure necessary for conformational variability. This realization makes it possible to make an enlightened analysis of the information inherent in the index and its influence on physical properties.

The fragments quantified by each $(\delta_i \, \delta_j \, \delta_k \, \delta_l)^{-0.5}$ value comprising the ^3X_p index may exhibit rotation around the central bond in the fragment. In the simplest three-bond molecule fragment, the butane skeleton, it is known that the molecule may assume a trans and two symmetry-equivalent gauche conformations. The energies are not the same; hence, the equilibrium conformation of an ensemble of molecules is a statistical weighted average of these conformers.

The value of $(\delta_i \, \delta_j \, \delta_k \, \delta_l)^{-0.5}$ for a fragment carries no information about the probable contributions of conformers to the equilibrium. The numerical values calculated for each fragment, however, reflect the degree of branching found at each of the four atoms in the fragment. To illustrate this point, we compare homologous alkane ^3X_p indexes and $(\delta_i \, \delta_j \, \delta_k \, \delta_l)^{-0.5}$ values with that of butane. In butane, the single fragment has delta values of

(1,2,2,1); hence, the calculated ^3X_p is 0.500. In n-pentane, there are two third-order fragments, each with delta values of (1,2,2,2). The calculated ^3X_p is 0.957. Higher homologs are formed by addition of fragments with deltas of (2,2,2,2); hence, the increment in the calculated ^3X_p indexes for each higher homolog is 0.250.

The value of ^3X_p for n-pentane is derived from two fragments but the values of $(\delta_i\,\delta_j\,\delta_k\,\delta_l)^{-0.5}$ for each fragment are less than that of the butane fragment. This is a result of the higher δ values at the two internal atoms of each fragment of pentane. As a consequence, pentane has a ^3X_p value less than twice that of butane.

The higher delta values at one end of each pentane fragment, relative to butane, parallel a greater number of conformational possibilities associated with bonds to that atom. In butane there are 3 conformations possible; in pentane, 7; in hexane, 12. These counts are sums of possible trans and gauche arrangements, while account is not taken of the relative energies favoring or prohibiting certain conformational possibilities. It is evident, however, that with a lengthening chain, equilibrium conformations encountered will have an increasing probability of having at least one gauche conformation. This is very likely, since there is only one all-trans conformation for each n-alkane, no matter what the length. Thus, it is generally appreciated that the average length of an n-alkane is some fraction of the fully extended length. The analysis reveals that the value of ^3X_p parallels the increasing number of possible gauche arrangements found in an homologous series.

Thus far, attention has focused on homologous alkanes and the increase in the value of ^3X_p accompanying the increasing number of conformational possibilities. In the case of branching in an alkane, the situation becomes more complex. In addition to the increase of ^3X_p due to homologation, at least one additional $(\delta_j\,\delta_j\,\delta_k\,\delta_l)^{-0.5}$ term is introduced at each branch point, for a constant chain length. If the branch point is at the third atom from the end of a chain in the molecule, the number of terms is increased by at least two, while adjacent branch points add at least four terms. Table 7

TABLE 7.   Effect of branching on third order fragment count, ^3N_p.

Alkane graph	^3N_p
	4
	5
	6
	8
	9

shows the effect of branching on the count of the number of $(\delta_i \delta_j \delta_k \delta_l)^{-0.5}$ terms for alkanes with a constant main chain length. This count is designated ^3N_p. The influence of branching among isomers is also evident. The number of $(\delta_i \delta_j \delta_k \delta_l)^{-0.5}$ terms, ^3N_p, for the nine isomers of heptane varies from 4 to 6 (see Table 8). Included in this table are the calculated values for ^3X_p and ^1X. Based on previous discussions, the ^3X_p values and the count of the number of $(\delta_i \delta_j \delta_k \delta_l)^{-0.5}$ terms should relate to the number of conformationally variable third order fragments. Thus 3E5 (3-ethylpentane) has six fragments capable of trans-gauche rotation and a ^3X_p of 1.732, while 24MM5 (2,4-dimethylpentane) has only four fragments and a ^3X_p value of 0.943.

TABLE 8. Effects of branching among heptanes and octanes on ^3N_p.

Alkane [a]	^3N_p	^3X_p	^1X	Z_g [b]	d_4^{20}
7	4	1.207	3.414		0.6838
3E5	6	1.732	3.346	3.48	0.6982
3M6	5	1.478	3.308	2.47	0.6871
2M6	4	1.135	3.270	1.64	0.6786
23MM5	6	1.782	3.181	3.55	0.6951
24MM5	4	0.943	3.126	2.40	0.6727
33MM5	6	1.914	3.121	4.00	0.6933
22MM5	4	1.000	3.061	2.00	0.6739
223MMM4	6	1.732	2.943		0.6901
224MMM5	5	1.021	3.417		0.69192
223MMM5	8	2.091	3.481		0.71602
233MMM5	9	2.474	3.504		0.72619
234MMM5	8	2.103	3.553		0.71906
22MM6	5	1.280	3.561	2.38	0.69528
25MM6	5	1.321	3.626	2.34	0.69354
24MM6	6	1.571	3.664	3.23	0.70036
23MM6	7	1.882	3.681	3.74	0.71214
33ME5	9	2.561	3.682	6.00	0.72442
34MM6	8	2.259	3.719	4.69	0.7192
23ME5	8	1.992	3.719	5.00	0.71932
2M7	5	1.352	3.770	1.93	0.69792
3M7	6	1.747	3.808	2.79	0.70582
3E6	7	1.747	3.808	2.79	0.70582
4M7	6	1.563	3.808	2.65	0.70463
3E6	7	1.852	3.846	3.75	0.71358

[a] See text for examples of abbreviations.
[b] Mann (1967).

B. Density Analysis

Without specifying what should be an energy-preferred conformation in either 3E5 or 24MM5, it can be stated that 3E5 has a greater number of possibilities for gauche folding. If we assume that the actual equilibrium conformation is a reflection of these possibilities then it might be concluded that 3E5 folds upon itself to a greater degree than does 24MM5. From this reasoning, it would be predicted that 3E5 would have a greater density than 24MM5. This is confirmed experimentally (see Table 8).

A more detailed analysis reveals that ^1X for the heptanes is not correlated with densities, while the ^3X_p indexes are.

$$d_4^{20} = 0.013 {}^1X + 0.644 \qquad r = 0.206, \ s = 0.0097, \ n = 9 \qquad (7)$$

$$d_4^{20} = 0.0237 {}^3X_p + 0.652 \qquad r = 0.948, \ s = 0.0032, \ n = 9 \qquad (8)$$

The results indicate that the count of potential gauche-trans conversions, the count of $(\delta_i \delta_j \delta_k \delta_l)^{-0.5}$ fragments, or the connectivity index derived from these fragments, ^3X_p, carries considerable information about the structural influence on density. This information is lacking in the ^1X index which is derived from a branching-weighted count of bonds. A combination of information from ^1X and the third order indexes, however, makes a significant improvement in the correlation:

$$d_4^{20} = 0.024 {}^3X_p + 0.016 {}^1X + 0.600 \qquad (9)$$
$$r = 0.983, \ s = 0.0020, \ n = 9$$

Mann (1967) has reported on a method of estimating the average number of gauche arrangements based on conformational possibilities weighted by a steric partition function. These values, Z_g, have been shown to rank densities, molar refraction and heats of combustion among branched alkanes.

An analysis of seven heptanes and twelve octanes using Z_g values reported by Mann, Table 8, reveals a good correlation with ^3X_p.

$$Z_g \text{ (heptanes)} = 2.227\,^3X_p - 0.427 \tag{10}$$
$$r = 0.946, \ s = 0.34, \ n = 7$$

$$Z_g \text{ (octanes)} = 3.019\,^3X_p - 1.81 \tag{11}$$
$$r = 0.950, \ s = 0.40, \ n = 12$$

C. Flexibility

The success demonstrated for ^3X_p in quantifying structural characteristics influencing density, led Kier and Hall (1983b) to consider this index as a possible descriptor of the somewhat more vague property referred to as flexibility, or its antonym, rigidity. The ^3X_p index correlates with the degree of folding of the molecule, in the pure state at one atmosphere, which manifests itself as the measured density. Flexibility on the other hand may be viewed as the potential for further folding of parts of the molecule beyond the equilibrium state seen in the density measurement. The latter property is akin to what has been referred to as the kinetic conformational flexibility (Luisi, 1977). It is a function of the rate of interconversion or the ease of interconversion due to energy barriers.

A flexibility index, F, should be a function of both the longest chain in the molecule, n, and the count of $(\delta_i\,\delta_j\,\delta_k\,\delta_l)^{-0.5}$ terms, which have been designated by the index ^3N_p. The flexibility of n-alkanes should increase with homologation while flexibility should decrease with branching. A suitable algorithm describing this is:

$$F = n/(1-1/^3N_p) \tag{12}$$

The calculated values of F in Table 9 reveal a logical set of expected values. Among n-alkanes, the value of F increases with homologation. Two-substituted alkanes are less flexible than the normal isomers while 3-substituted alkanes are less flexible still. The algorithm has a minimum; hence, it is not useful for butane, 2-methyl butane or pentane. The index reflects a weighted count of non-terminal bonds capable of rotation to give gauche or trans conformers. The weighting favors a methylene-methylene bond, while a methine-methylene bond contributes less to the numerical value. The assumption is that the greater the substitution at an internal carbon atom, the less free the rotation. This is the essence of the flexibility described by the index. As an example, the F for 2M5 is 7.50 while for 3M5 it is 6.67. The greater flexibility predicted for 2M5 is a consequence of internal bonds described by delta values of (3,2) and (2,2). For the 3M5 isomer, the internal bonds are described by delta values of (2,3) and (2,3). For another substituted pentane, 23MM5, there are internal bonds of (3,3) and (3,2). The F value for this isomer is 6.00. The F value is proposed as an index predicting kinetic conformational flexibility.

4. Information from $^4X_{pc}$ and $^4X^V_{pc}$

A. Calculation

The index is calculated using the standard algorithm described in Chapter 1. Each atom in the fragment is assigned a value based on the number of atoms bonded to it (adjacency) in the original molecule. A valence delta (δ^V) is assigned on the basis of adjacency or, in the case of heteroatoms or unsaturated carbons, use of the prescription $\delta^V = Z^V - h$ where Z^V is the number of valence electrons and h is the number of attached hydrogen atoms. The $^4X_{pc}$ index then is computed $^4X_{pc} = \Sigma (\delta_i \delta_j \delta_k \delta_l \delta_m)^{-0.5}$.

TABLE 9. Flexibility index for several alkanes.

Alkane	^3N_p a)	F	Alkane	^3N_p a)	F
6	3	9.00	3E6	7	8.17
2M5	3	7.50	23ME5	8	6.86
3M5	4	6.67	33ME5	9	6.75
22MM4	3	6.00	23MM6	7	7.00
23MM4	4	5.33	22MM6	5	7.50
7	4	9.33	24MM6	6	7.20
2M6	4	8.00	25MM6	5	7.50
3M6	5	7.50	233MMM5	9	5.62
3E5	6	7.20	2233MMMM4	9	4.50
23MM5	6	6.00	9	6	10.80
24MM5	4	6.67	2M8	6	9.60
33MM5	6	6.00	3M8	7	9.33
22MM5	4	6.67	33EE5	12	7.64
223MMM4	6	4.80	233MMM6	10	6.67
8	5	10.00	2334MMMM5	12	5.45
2M7	5	8.75	10	7	11.67
3M7	6	8.40	11	8	12.57

a) In the case of 3E5, there are two longest chains of five carbons in length. One is added to n for the presence of an additional non-terminal carbon; thus, n for 3E5 = 6. For 33EE5, n = 7 in eqn. 12. In the case of 2,2,3,3MMMM4, there are four equivalent, four-carbon longest chains; however, none of these involves an additional non-terminal carbon; hence, n = 4.

Likewise, the $^4X_{pc}^V$ index is computed using δ^V values. The index carries information about the number of benzene ring substituents, the substitution pattern, the length of the substituents up to three bond lengths, and the heteroatom type of substituent, Kier (1980b).

B. Orientation of Ring Substituents

The $^4X_{pc}$ index encodes information about the orientation of ring substituents. In general, the greater the adjacency or crowding of substituents, the larger is the numerical value of the $^4X_{pc}$ index. For the six trisubstituted rings, 3-8, in Table 10, the number of adjacent pairs of substituents versus the $^4X_{pc}$ values shows an increase in value with an increased pairing of the substituents. The same effect is evident with the five tetrasubstituted rings, 9-13, in Table 10. The use of $^4X_{pc}$ may be a meaningful way of quantifying crowding or adjacency of ring substituents.

C. Length of Ring Substituents

The effect of substituent length on the numerical value of $^4X_{pc}$ is illustrated by two series of compounds. With the ortho-substituted series (1, 14, and 15), lengthening the chain by one atom results in a consistent decrease in the $^4X_{pc}$ value. With the meta-substituted series (2, 16, and 17), there is a decline in the $^4X_{pc}$ value beyond one bond length. Substituents with bond lengths of four or more are not distinguishable from those of three-bond length. On the other hand, a branched substituent such as an isopropyl group gives rise to additional $^4X_{pc}$ fragments and, hence, to an increased numerical value of this index. An interesting observation can be made about the $^4X_{pc}$ indexes and structures discussed in these two series. A ranking of these six compounds based on the extent of interaction between substituent groups is speculated to be 1, 14, 15, 17, 16, and 2. This ranking closely parallels the decline in the value of their respective $^4X_{pc}$ indexes.

TABLE 10. Molecular connectivity indexes for substituted benzenes.

No.	Molecule	$^4X_{pc}$	$^4X_{pc}^v$	No.	Molecule	$^4X_{pc}$	$^4X_{pc}^v$
1.		1.020	0.561	12.		1.772	1.001
2.		0.777	0.390	13.		2.053	1.173
3.		1.638	0.942	14.		0.992	0.554
4.		1.360	0.729	15.		0.943	0.524
5.		1.369	0.732	16.		0.873	0.455
6.		1.500	0.856	17.		0.813	0.421
7.		1.514	0.821	18.	NH_2	1.020	0.404
8.		1.047	0.535	19.	H_2N	0.777	0.314
9.		2.245	1.317	20.	H_2N-	0.841	0.331
10.		1.919	1.089	21.	OH	1.020	0.356
11.		2.127	1.240	22.	Cl	1.020	0.633

D. Heteroatom Substituents

From Table 10, it can be seen that 18, 21 and 22 have the same $^4X_{pc}$ index since all three are similarly substituted derivatives with the same number of bonds. The valence level index $^4X_{pc}^v$ must be employed to differentiate between substituents containing atoms of differing δ^v values; thus, 18, 21, and 22 have different $^4X_{pc}^v$ indexes. The larger the δ^v for the heteroatom in these molecules, the smaller is the numerical value of the $^4X_{pc}^v$ index. The $^4X_{pc}^v$ index adds the presence of hetereoatoms in the substituent groups to the information encoded in the $^4X_{pc}$ index. In addition, the $^4X_{pc}^v$ index can distinguish between substituents containing the same heteroatoms but in different group positions.

5. Higher Order Path Indexes

The indexes ^4X_p and ^5X_p and higher order indexes have appeared in regression analyses. Their presence can be interpreted to imply that a critical dimension or number of carbon atoms in a chain is influential in the structure, influencing the property.

One study that revealed this information (Kier and Hall, 1978) was performed on a large series of molecules with the general formula:

$$R_1-CH_2-CH_2-R_2$$

There were 14 variants reflected by R_1 and up to 8 variants in R_2. This resulted in a matrix of 104 compounds. The lack of a relation between R_1 and R_2 was deduced from the finding that the indexes, ^4X_p, ^5X_p, and ^6X_p, were not significant in a multiple term regression analysis. These indexes are derived from fragments long enough in number of atoms to bridge the variable structures R_1 and R_2. The presence of ^5X_p and ^6X_p as significant terms would imply that R_1 and R_2 are linked in some cases, resulting a single structural fragment which influenced activity of some of the molecules. The conclusion based upon their absence in the analysis was that structural features R_1 and R_2 are independent in their influence on activity.

In a second study on the specific anosmia to fatty acids (Kier et al, 1977), a three term equation was found to contain the term ^5X_p. The interpretation is that fatty acids with five or more carbon atoms have a negative effect on the activity, whereas smaller fatty acids, without a chain length long enough to result in a fifth order fragment, have activities dependent only upon the other equation terms.

In a third study, the ^6X_p index by itself gave a high correlation ($r = 0.95$) with antiviral potency among substituted benzimidazoles (Hall and Kier, 1978). Hall and Kier interpreted this equation term to mean that 2,5-disubstituted molecules had a higher potency than other substitution configurations. It is obvious that this substitition pattern results in an extra sixth order fragment relative to a 2,4 (or 2,7) substitution pattern.

In a study on ether toxicity, it was found that a quadratic expression:

$$pC = 1.444\,^1X^V - 0.208(^1X^V)^2 + 0.462 \qquad (13)$$

could be replaced with an equation containing a higher order index:

$$pC = 0.676\,^1X^V - 1.403\,^5X_p^V + 1.132 \qquad (14)$$

with the same precision (Kier and Hall, 1976). The fifth order index encodes the information that molecules with fifth and higher order fragments diminish the potency of the molecules in the study. In this case, the use of $^5X_p^V$ is more informative and lends itself to more direct interpretation of structural influences on biological activity.

6. Other Connectivity Indexes

A. ^3X_c Index

An early expectation was that the ^3X_c index, encoding information about the number of branch points in a molecule, would be a prominent term in structure-activity regression analyses. Interestingly, this has not been the case. A comparison with the $^4X_{pc}$ index for substituted benzenes revealed that the latter index was richer in information content (Kier, 1980b).

Reflection on the structural fragment represented by ^3X_c reveals that for each fragment there is a corresponding atom in the molecule with a $\delta = 3$. The ^1X index for such a molecule would contain three fragment values of $(3\ \delta_i)^{-0.5}$, $(3\ \delta_j)^{-0.5}$ and $(3\ \delta_k)^{-0.5}$. This aspect of the structural information is duplicated in the ^1X index. In the case of the neopentane skeleton there are four fragments contributing to the ^3X_c index. Again, the ^1X index would repeat this information. In summary, it is probable that the ^3X_c index lacks unique information and that ^1X would most likely appear in regression analyses as a more prominent term.

B. Chain Indexes

The chain terms have been introduced to encode the presence of ring fragments. At this time, nothing more can be said beyond the observation that these indexes are indicator variables encoding the presence of a ring of a specified size.

7. Summary

The molecular connectivity indexes have been shown to be rich in structural information related to topological, geometric and spatial attributes. The relative branching of a molecule is encoded in ^1X indexes when compared to structural isomers. This translates into an encoding of molecular bulk or volume and molecular surface area.

To the extent that these hard-sphere geometric characteristics have meaning, the first order indexes are capable of relating closely to them. The ^{0}X indexes encode information about atoms or points, the ^{2}X indexes carry information about 3-atom fragments which are the minimum number necessary to describe a plane, while the $^{3}X_p$ indexes encode information about a three-dimensional attribute such as conformation. The $^{4}X_{pc}$ index encodes information useful to the structure analysis of substituted rings. Information such as degree of substitution, proximity of substituents, length and heteroatom content of these groups is contained in $^{4}X_{pc}$ and $^{4}X_{pc}^{v}$ indexes. From QSAR equations derived from regression analyses, it is easy to interpret the model in terms of familiar molecular fragments. This is the basic information that a chemist must have in order to proceed in the drug design process.

References

Bondi, A. (1964). Van der Waals volumes and radii. J. Phys. Chem. 68, 441-451.

Hall, L. H. and Kier, L. B. (1978). Molecular connectivity and substructure analysis. J. Pharm. Sci., 67, 1743-1747.

Hall, L. H. and Kier, L. B. (1981). The relation of molecular connectivity to molecular volume and biological activity. Eur. J. Med. Chem. 16, 399-407.

Hermann, R. B. (1972). The correlation of hydrocarbon solubility in water with solvent cavity surface area. J. Phys. Chem. 76, 2754-2759.

Kier, L. B. (1980a) in Physical Chemical Properties of Drugs. (Edited by S. H. Yalkowsky et al., Ed.) p. 285, Marcel-Dekker, New York.

Kier, L. B. (1980b). Structural information from molecular connectivity $^4X_{pc}$ index. J. Pharm. Sci., 69, 1034-1039.

Kier, L. B., DiPaolo, T. and Hall, L. H. (1977). Structure-activity studies on odor molecules using molecular connectivity. J. Theor. Biol. 67, 585-595.

Kier, L. B. and Hall, L. H. (1976). Molecular Connectivity in Chemistry and Drug Research. Academic, New York.

Kier, L. B. and Hall, L. H. (1978). A molecular connectivity study of the muscarinic receptor affinity of acetylcholine antagonists. J. Pharm. Sci., 67, 1408-1412.

Kier, L. B. and Hall, L. H. (1981). Derivation and significance of valence molecular connectivity. J. Pharm. Sci., 70, 583-589.

Kier, L. B. and Hall, L. H. (1983a). General definition of valence delta values for molecular connectivity. J. Pharm. Sci. 72, 1170-1173.

Kier, L. B. and Hall, L. H. (1983b). Structural information and a flexibility index from the molecular connectivity ^3X_p index. Quant. Struct.-Act. Relat. 2, 55-59.

Luisi, P. L. (1977). Molecular conformational rigidity: an approach to quantification. Naturwis. 64, 569-574.

Mann, G. (1967). Conformation and physical data of alkanes and cycloalkanes. Tetrahedron. 23, 3375-3392.

Randic, M. (1975). On characterization of molecular branching. J. Am. Chem. Soc., 97, 6609-6615.

CHAPTER 4
Electronic Information

1. Electron Counts from Delta Values

We have shown in Chapter 3 that the delta values of atoms in their valence or hybrid state reflect counts of orbitals. More precisely, the orbitals enumerated are those of non-hydrogen sigma electrons, lone pair electrons, and pi bonding electrons. This information is encoded into a series of topological descriptions of molecules when the delta values are utilized in the algorithms for molecular connectivity indexes. Prominent among this information are volume-related attributes. In terms of physical properties, it has been shown that molecular connectivity indexes correlate well with physical properties dependent upon volume.

If the count of occupied valence state orbitals is encoded in delta values, then it logically follows that the delta values simultaneously count the electrons associated with the orbitals. Accordingly, we can expect that the delta values contain a rich amount of electronic information about atoms in their valence state. This information can be revealed by examining each of the two cardinal numbers or delta values associated with each atom. The simple delta value, δ, is a count of non-hydrogen bonding sigma electrons, $\sigma - h$, associated with an atom in its valence state. Hence, $\delta = \sigma$ when no hydrogens are sigma bonded. Table 1 shows the delta values and the count of electrons for carbon, nitrogen and oxygen in their various valence states.

TABLE 1.   Categories of electrons on atoms in their valence states when no hydrogens are bonded.

Atom	Valence State	Z^V	δ^V	δ	σ	π	n
C	sp^3	4	4	4	4	0	0
	sp^2	4	4	3	3	1	0
	sp	4	4	2	2	2	0
N	sp^3	5	5	3	3	0	2
	sp^2	5	5	2	2	1	2
	sp	5	5	1	1	2	2
O	sp^3	6	6	2	2	0	4
	sp^2	6	6	1	1	1	4

The valence δ^V by definition is $(Z^V - h)$, where Z^V is the count of all valence electrons and h is the count of bonding hydrogens. If we consider only atoms without hydrogens, then $\delta^V = Z^V$; hence, δ^V is a count of valence electrons. It follows that all valence electrons not of the sigma type must be in pi or lone pair orbitals. These counts and their interrelation are found in Table 1. In terms of deltas, $(\delta^V - \delta)$ is a count of pi and lone pair electrons. We can certainly expect that the number and orbital distribution of electrons influence electronic characteristics associated with atoms in their valence state.

2.   Estimation of Valence State Electronegativity

A well known electronic property of a bonded atom in a molecule is electronegativity. Pauling (1932) proposed this concept and defined it as a measure of the power of a chemically bonded atom to attract electrons to itself. Several measures of this characteristic were suggested, the most satisfactory being that of Mulliken (1934). He defined electronegativity, X_M, as the average value of the ionization potential and the electron affinity. Expressed in electron volts, this value was computed by Hinze and Jaffe (1962) for atoms in their bonding valence states. The electronegativity scale of Pauling is more familiar to chemists, but does not distinguish among hybrid states of the same atom, although they certainly have different electronegativities.

Figure 1 shows some Mulliken electronegativity values superimposed on a δ, δ^V plot of second-row atoms in their valence state. Inspection reveals some obvious trends. For a constant $\delta^V = 4$, the values $\delta = 2$, 3, and 4 describe sp, sp^2, and sp^3 carbon atoms, respectively. Electronegativity diminishes in the same order. This electronic effect manifests itself in the decreasing acidity of the bonds:

$$\equiv C-H > \ =C-H > \ -C-H$$

As δ^V decreases for constant δ values, electronegativity also decreases. The trends suggest that electronegativity is some function of $\delta^V - \delta$. For the nine second-row atom valence states in Figure 1, the following relationship obtains:

$$X_M = 2.05 \ (\delta^V - \delta) + 6.99 \tag{1}$$
$$r = 0.989, \ s = 0.60, \ n = 9, \ F = 305$$

This correlation is excellent, with the standard deviation being of the same order magnitude as the X_M standard deviation of Hinze and Jaffe (1962), due to uncertainties in the electron affinities. The intercept is close to the electronegativity of hydrogen (7.17 eV), which would have a $\delta^V - \delta$ value of zero. The interpretation of eqn. (1) is clear. The electronegativity of an atom in its valence state is closely related to the number of electrons in pi and lone pair orbitals. This is an estimate called the Kier/Hall electronegativity (Kier and Hall, 1981).

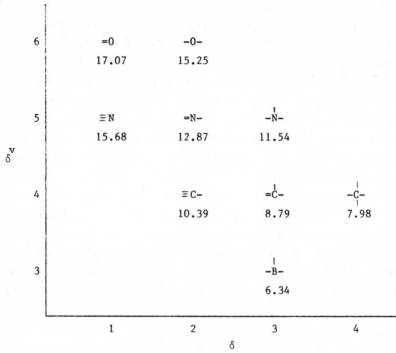

FIGURE 1.   Relationship of δ and δ^V to Mulliken valence state electronegativities (eV) for second quantum level atoms.

The information in $\delta^V - \delta$ is evident from the equations defining delta values:

$$\delta^V = \sigma + p + n - h \tag{2}$$

$$\delta = \sigma - h \tag{3}$$

$$\delta^V - \delta = p + n \tag{4}$$

where σ is the number of the bonding electrons in sigma-type orbitals, n, the count of lone pair electrons and p, the count of pi electrons. The observation that the electronegativity of a bound atom is related to the presence of pi and lone pair electrons leads to the conclusion that these electrons are less effective than sigma electrons in screening the core charge. This follows from the fact that electronegativity manifests itself through sigma bonds; thus, valence electrons outside of these orbitals leave the core charge, $+Z^V$, less screened than when all valence electrons are sigma bonding, as in Csp^3.

The relationship can be made more general to include atoms of other rows by realizing that the nuclear attraction for valence electrons (hence, the electronegativity) must be related to their distance from the nucleus and the screening effect of intervening electrons. This distance effect may be approximated by the square of the principal quantum number, N in the denominator. The general expression relating the Mulliken electronegativities to the delta values for 19 atom valence states of the first, second, and third rows, which are prominent in forming covalent bonds, takes the form:

$$X_M = 7.99 \; (\delta^V - \delta)/N^2 + 7.07 \qquad (5)$$
$$r = 0.988, \; s = 0.48, \; n = 19, \; F = 600$$

The δ^V value in eqn. (5) for third-row atoms is defined as $\delta^V = (Z^V - h)$. The usual expression $\delta^V = (Z^V - h) / (Z^V - Z - 1)$ is not used since the use of N^2 corrects for the distance of the valence electrons from the nucleus and is more useful in relating the electronegativity directly to the count of pi and lone pair electrons, $\delta^V - \delta$.

The experimental and calculated results are shown in Table 2. The fifth column in Table 2, $(\delta^V - \delta)/N^2$, is the Kier/Hall valence state electronegativity. This value can be compared to the Pauling estimate of electronegativity by adding approximately 2.5 to the value, although the Pauling value is for an atom irrespective of the valence state.

TABLE 2. Delta values of valence state atoms and Mulliken electronegativities.

Atom	Hybrid State	δ^V	δ	$\dfrac{\delta^V-\delta}{N^2}$	$X_M(ev)$ [a]	X_M calc.(ev)
H	s	1	1	0	7.17	7.05
B	sp^2	3	3	0	6.34	7.05
C	sp	4	2	0.50	10.39	11.04
	sp^2	4	3	0.25	8.79	9.05
	sp^3	4	4	0	7.98	7.05
N	sp	5	1	1.00	15.68	15.04
	sp^2	5	2	0.75	12.87	13.04
	sp^3	5	3	0.50	11.54	11.04
O	sp^2	6	1	1.25	17.07	17.04
	sp^3	6	2	1.00	15.25	15.04
Si	sp	4	2	0.22	9.06	8.82
	sp^2	4	3	0.11	7.90	7.93
	sp^3	4	4	0	7.30	7.05
P	sp	5	1	0.44	11.35	10.60
	sp^2	5	2	0.33	9.67	9.71
	sp^3	5	3	0.22	8.90	8.82
S	sp^2	6	1	0.55	10.88	11.49
	sp^3	6	2	0.44	10.14	10.60
Cl	sp^3	7	1	0.66	11.84	12.37

[a] Calculated by Hinze and Jaffe (1962).

To conclude, it is stated that the number derived from $\delta_i^V - \delta_i$ for atom i describes a structural index for a valence state atom closely approximating the electronegativity. Also, we have shown that the number derived from $\delta_i^V + \delta_i$ for atom i describes a structural index for a valence state atom closely approximating the van der Waals volume contribution to the molecule. Mathematically, $\delta_i^V - \delta_i$ and $\delta_i^V + \delta_i$ are orthogonal; that is, they are independent of each other. This orthogonality corresponds to the observation that the Bondi volume and the Mulliken electronegativities autocorrelate only to the extent of $r^2 = 0.21$.

3. Derivation of The Bond Index from Electronegativity Equalization

The δ^V and δ values for atoms in their valence states encode information about the electronegativity of atoms. The electronegativity of atoms in bonds influences several properties including ionicity, bond dipole, partial atomic charge, and bond strength, all resulting from electronegativity equalization (Sanderson, 1954). The calculation of molecular connectivity indexes as a sum of bond indexes thus incorporates some information about electronic structure, encoded in the delta values. With the structural and physical significance of δ^V and δ revealed, it is possible to show a derivation of the bond index ($\delta_i \delta_j)^{-0.5}$ which encodes information about bond structure and properties. The properties encoded in δ_A^V for an atom A are considered to be contributed equally from all valence electrons. Thus, one electron from atom A forming one bond A-B will possess the fraction $1/\delta_A^V$ of the properties encoded by δ_A^V. Atom B brings to the same bond the fraction $1/\delta_B^V$. In forming bond A-B, these orbitals will become adjusted toward a more equal intermediate electronegativity, which may be ascribed to the bond.

The principle of electronegativity equalization was set forth by Sanderson (1954), who proposed that the geometric mean of the atom electronegativities leads to the best description of the bond electronegativity. From Sanderson (1954) (1976), $(1/\delta_A^V \; 1/\delta_B^V)^{-0.5}$ is the algorithm appropriate for two bonded atoms. This algorithm is identical to the molecular connectivity description of a bond as shown in Chapter 1.

4. Electronic Information Encoded in $^1X^V$

The index for the molecule, $^1X^V$, is written as a summation of the bond terms, $^1X^V = \Sigma \; (\delta_i \delta_j)^{-0.5}$. This is the valence molecular connectivity index of first order since it is summed over all bonds that are single-path fragments of the molecule. Valence molecular connectivity is built on the sigma electron framework of the molecule. The presence of an atom i with non-sigma valence electrons (pi or lone-pair electrons) results in the term $1/\delta^V_i$ being smaller than $1/\delta_i$. The value of $^1X^V$ for the molecule containing atom i with non-sigma electrons reflects the total number of bonds and their adjacency, but it also reflects the diminished value of $1/\delta^V_i$ relative to $1/\delta_i$ due to the presence of non-sigma electrons on atom i.

From the examples in Table 3, a series of comparisons reveal the encoded electronic information in $^1X^V$ values. Molecule 1, butane, is the reference structure where all $\delta^V = \delta$; hence, $^1X^V = {}^1X = 1.914$. There are no non-sigma electrons so $^1X - {}^1X^V = 0$.

Molecules 2 and 3 in Table 3 are four-atom amines (excluding hydrogens), each with two non-sigma electrons on the nitrogen. Since the positions of the nitrogen atoms in the chains are different in each case, the fractional contributions of valence electrons forming non-hydrogenic bonds are different. The nitrogen in molecule 2 contributes one-third, $(1/\delta^V_N) = 1/3$, of its non-hydrogenic valence electrons to form one sigma bond to carbon. The nitrogen in molecule 3, contributes one-fourth, $(1/\delta^V_N) = 1/4$, of its non-hydrogenic valence electrons to each of two sigma bonds with adjacent carbons. The indexes for bonds B-C and C-D thus are different for these cases. As a consequence, the $^1X^V$ indexes are different for molecules 2 and 3, and each, in turn, is different and less than the value for molecule 1.

TABLE 3. Information encoded in $^1X^V$ and δ^V values for four-atom molecules with δ values of $A^1-B^2-C^2-D^1$.

No.	Molecule	Atom δ^V Values				$^1X^V$	Non-sigma Electrons	$^1X-^1X^V$
		A	B	C	D			
1	$CH_3CH_2CH_2CH_3$	1	2	2	1	1.914	0	0
2	$CH_3CH_2CH_2NH_2$	1	2	2	3	1.615	2	0.299
3	$CH_3CH_2NHCH_3$	1	2	4	1	1.561	2	0.353
4	$CH_3CH_2CH_2OH$	1	2	2	5	1.523	4	0.391
5	$CH_3CH_2OCH_3$	1	2	6	1	1.404	4	0.510
6	$CH_3CH_2CHCH_2$	1	2	3	2	1.524	2	0.390
7	$CH_3CHCHCH_3$	1	3	3	1	1.488	2	0.426
8	CH_3CH_2CHO	1	2	3	6	1.351	6	0.563
9	CH_3CH_2CCH	1	2	4	3	1.349	4	0.565
10	CH_3CCCH_3	1	4	4	1	1.250	4	0.664
11	$HOCH_2CH_2OH$	5	2	2	5	1.132	8	0.782
12	CH_3CHNOH	1	3	5	5	1.036	8	0.878
13	$OCHCHO$	6	3	3	6	0.805	12	1.109

Viewed in terms of valence electron structure information, it is obvious that in molecule 2 the nitrogen bonds only once to a carbon and, therefore, participates only once as an amine group in an electronegativity equalization event. In molecule 3, the nitrogen is located mid-chain and, therefore, participates in two bonds to carbons, with two opportunities to participate in electronegativity equalization. Clearly, electronically governed properties differ and are possibly correlated with the $^1X^V$ values. The formation of two sigma bonds by nitrogen in molecule 3 leads to two electronegativity equalization events, resulting in a greater buildup of charge on the nitrogen in molecule 3. Thus, molecule 3 is more basic than molecule 2. Within closely related amines, the $^1X - ^1X^V$ difference appears to parallel this effect. It follows that $^1X - ^1X^V$ for trimethylamine is 0.390, suggesting that it is more basic than molecule 3. This is true in the gas phase.

The two amines, molecules 2 and 3, have the same number and kind of atoms. They differ from the reference structure, butane, by having two non-sigma electrons on one atom. The calculated $^1X^V$ value reflects both the presence of the non-sigma electrons and the adjacency relationship of that atom (nitrogen) to other atoms in the molecule. The diminished value of $^1X^V$ for molecule 3, relative to butane and to its positional isomeric amine, molecule 2, parallels structural differences that can be interpreted in electronic terms such as relative charge and basicity.

In molecules 4 and 5, oxygen is the atom contributing non-sigma electrons to the molecules. The adjacency effect mimics the amines. The terminal oxygen in molecule 4 with six valence electrons has a bonded hydrogen; hence, $\delta^V = Z^V - h = 6 - 1 = 5$. Thus, $(1/\delta^V) = 1/5$ describes the sigma electron fraction forming a hydroxyl oxygen bond to a carbon. Only one sigma bond involves the hydroxyl oxygen group. In molecule 5, the δ^V for oxygen is 6; hence, $1/\delta^V = 1/6$ describes each of two sigma electrons bonding to two adjacent carbons. Electronegativity equalization is possible through two bonds in molecule 5 but only one in molecule 4. The greater $^1X - ^1X^V$ calculated for molecule 5 reflects the consequences of this greater degree of adjacency. Note also that the $^1X^V$ for molecule 4 is less than that of molecule 2 (and 5 is less than that of 3), reflecting more non-sigma electrons in the oxygen-containing molecules. A physical manifestation mirroring this result is the lower ionization potentials of ethers relative to alcohols, and secondary amines relative to primary amines, of the same size. A lone pair electron is the one lost in this process.

Molecules 6 and 7 in Table 3 portray a different situation. In these alkenes there are two non-sigma electrons in each molecule, but they are not paired on the same atom, as with the amines; they are located on adjacent atoms. Thus, the δ^V values for molecule 6 are different from the reference butane structure in the case of two atoms. This situation is typical of an unsaturated bond. As a consequence, of the three bond indexes calculated for each alkene molecule, two differ from the reference butane molecule in the case of molecule 6 and all three differ in the case of molecule 7. The $^1X^V$ for molecule 7 is lower than that for molecule 6, consistent with a greater availability of the pi electrons. As a consequence, molecule 7 reacts faster with electrophiles, has a lower heat of hydrogenation and a lower ionization potential, than molecule 6.

5. Group Values of Electronegativity

A. General Formula

Electronegativity manifests itself along bonds. Differences in electronegativity between a pair of bonded atoms result in some electronegativity equalization (Sanderson, 1951) accomplished by charge displacement (Huheey 1965, 1966). The effect of equalization may be estimated as follows, using the hydroxyl group as an example. From Table 2, the Kier/Hall electronegativity, E^σ, of oxygen sp^3 is 1.0, while that of hydrogen is 0.0. Electron density flows to the more electronegative oxygen atom. The difference in electronegativities, $E_H^\sigma - E^\sigma (Osp^3)$, alters the electronegativity of oxygen through the influence along one sigma bond. Thus, approximately $1/Z^V$ or 1/6 of the valence electrons of oxygen are influenced directly by the presence of a bonded H. The influence of H on O may be estimated:

$$E_{OH}^\sigma = E^\sigma (Osp^3) + 1/Z_0^V (E_H^\sigma - E^\sigma (Osp^3))$$
$$E_{OH}^\sigma = 1.0 + 1/6 (0 - 1.0)$$
$$E_{OH}^\sigma = 0.83$$

The less electronegative hydrogen atom serves to decrease the electronegativity of the oxygen atom, and so the –OH group is less electronegative than an isolated oxygen atom in the sp^3 state. For the general case for group –A–B:

$$E^\sigma_{AB} = E^\sigma_A + 1/Z^V_A \ (E^\sigma_B - E^\sigma_A) \tag{6}$$

For group –A–B–C, the modified E^σ_B is calculated first in the same manner as shown for –OH, then its influence on E^σ_A is calculated as above. E^σ_{AB} is thus a calculated value of the electronegativity of atom A (bonded to another moiety) modified through its sigma bond to another atom such as B.

Examples of two group electronegativity calculations illustrate the model:

$$E^\sigma(NH_2) = E^\sigma(Nsp^3) + 2/Z^V(E^\sigma(H) - E^\sigma(Nsp^3)) = 0.30$$

$$E^\sigma(OCH_3) = E^\sigma(Osp^3) + 1/Z^V_0 \ (E^\sigma(CH_3) - E^\sigma(Osp^3)) = 0.83$$

B. Benzene Substituent Value

If E^σ_{AB} symbolizes a calculated group electronegativity operating through σ bonds, the effect of the group on a benzene ring should be reflected in part by this value. It is known that benzene substituents influence the ring through both sigma and sometimes pi bonds. The influence on the ring from electrons in orbitals of pi symmetry requires a further analysis.

C. Substituent Effect Through π Symmetry Orbitals

The orbital on atom X which is spatially disposed to overlap with the benzene ring will contribute or attract electron density through this pi bond. In addition to the E^σ effect, the effect of such an

atom on the ring may be due to: 1) the difference in electronegativity between the pi orbital on a substituent atom and the pi
orbital on the ring carbon (E^{π}); or 2) the occurrence on a
substituent atom of a lone pair of electrons, applying pressure on
the ring due to the presence of the two non-bonded electrons (E^n).
These two effects plus the inductive effect through the sigma bond
(E^{σ}) result in the observed electronic effect of the atom (group) on
the ring. The total substituent effect may be written as a simple
sum with the recognition that the coefficient of E^n is negative:

$$\text{Total Substituent Effect} = aE^{\sigma} + bE^{\pi} - cE^n \tag{7}$$

To approximate the pi electron effect, it is necessary to compare
the relative electronegativities of the X pi orbitals and the ring
carbon pi orbital. Data from Hinze and Jaffe (1963) reveal that pi
orbital electronegativities are 1/2 to 2/3 the value of the
corresponding hybrid sigma orbitals on the same atom. The ranking
of pi orbital electronegativities within a quantum level, however,
parallel those of the corresponding sigma orbital electronegativities.
As a consequence, the difference in electronegativities between the
pi orbital on atom X and the carbon (ring) may be approximated by:

$$(E^{\pi}_X - E^{\pi}_{Csp}2) = k \ (E^{\sigma}_X - E^{\sigma}_{Csp}2) \tag{8}$$

This can be evaluated by comparing Mulliken X^{σ}_M and X^{π}_M values
shown in Table 4. If we confine our attention to singly occupied pi
orbitals overlapping with a phenyl ring carbon pi orbital, then
divalent N and trivalent O will never be found as ring substituents
in neutral molecules. The remaining three pi orbitals, divalent C as
well as trivalent C and N, have ratios which deviate less than 10%
from the average ratio of 0.59. Thus, a fair approximation of E^{π}_X
can be expressed:

$$E^{\pi}_X = k \ E^{\sigma}_X \tag{9}$$

where k is approximately 0.6.

TABLE 4.   Electronegativities of sigma and pi orbitals.

Hybrid Atom	X_M^{σ}(eV)	X_M^{π}(eV)	X_M^{π}/X_M^{σ}
C sp	10.39	5.65	0.54
C sp^2	8.79	5.60	0.64
N sp	15.68	7.92	0.51
N sp^2	12.87	7.95	0.62
O sp^2	17.07	10.09	0.59

From these relationships, the value of E_{XY} can be approximated by:

$$E_{XY}^{\pi} = 0.6E_X^{\sigma} + 0.6(E_Y^{\sigma} - E_X^{\sigma}) \tag{10}$$

This relation applies only to those atoms with orbitals involved in conjugation with the ring.

D.   Lone Pair Electron Effect

A final term must be considered in eqn. (7), the E_{XY}^n effect due to lone pair electrons on atom X. In this case the symmetry-allowed hybrid orbital or pi orbitals on atom X, available for overlap, is doubly occupied and of low electronegativity; hence, the effect is donation to the ring. The extent of pressure on the ring must be related to the electronegativity of atom X; hence, an approximation of the lone pair effect might be $E^n = 2 - E_X^{\sigma}$. This expression approximates the third term in eqn. (7).

The expanded equation for the substituent effect of S_{XY} is:

$$S = a \ [E_X^{\sigma} + 1/Z_X^v(E_Y^{\sigma} - E_X^{\sigma})] + b \ [0.6E_X^{\sigma} + 0.6(E_Y^{\sigma} - E_X^{\sigma})]$$
$$+ \ c \ (2 - E_X^{\sigma}) \tag{11}$$

It should be stated that the partition of the substituent effect into these factors based upon calculated electronegativity influences does not necessarily parallel the factoring of Hammett sigma constants into σ_I and σ_R or the Swain-Lupton F and R contributions. Thus, E^{σ} may not relate precisely to σ_I or F. However, the linear combination of contributions as modeled above, may relate to the experimentally observed Hammett substituent constant for the para position (σ_p) and the meta position (σ_m).

E. Examples of Total Substituent Effect Calculations

$-CH=CH_2$

$$E^{\sigma} = E^{\sigma} \ (Csp^2) + 1/Z_C^v \ [E^{\sigma}(H) - E^{\sigma}(Csp^2)] \ +$$
$$1/Z_C^v[E^{\sigma}(CH_2) - E^{\sigma}(Csp^2)]$$
$$= 0.25 + 1/4(0-0.25) + 1/4 \ (0.125-0.25)$$
$$E^{\sigma} = 0.16$$
$$E^{\pi} = 0.6E^{\sigma}(Csp^2) + 0.6[E^{\sigma} \ (Csp^2) - E^{\sigma}(Csp^2)]$$
$$E^{\pi} = 0.15$$

$-CHO$

$$E^{\sigma} = E^{\sigma}(Csp^2) + 1/Z_C^v[E^{\sigma}(H) - E^{\sigma}(Csp^2)] \ +$$
$$1/Z_C^v \ [E^{\sigma}(Osp^2) - E^{\sigma}(Csp^2)]$$
$$= 0.25 + 1/4 \ (0-0.25) + 1/4(1.25-0.25)$$
$$E^{\sigma} = 0.44$$
$$E^{\pi} = 0.6E^{\sigma}(Csp^2) + 0.6 \ [E^{\sigma}(Osp^2) - E^{\sigma}(Csp^2)]$$
$$= 0.6(0.25 + 0.6(1.0)$$
$$E^{\pi} = 0.75$$

$-OCH_3$

$$E^{\sigma} = E^{\sigma}(Osp^3) + 1/Z_0^V \ [E^{\sigma}(CH_3) - E^{\sigma}(Osp^3)]$$
$$= 1.0 + 1/6 \ (0-1.0)$$
$$E = 0.83$$
$$E^n = 2 - E^{\sigma}(Osp^3)$$
$$= 2-1.0$$
$$E^n = 1.0$$

F. Prediction of Hammett Substituent Values

A test of the possible significance of the calculated total substituent effect, S, eqn. (11), can be made by comparison with measured Hammett sigma values. Both Hammett σ_p and σ_m values are selected from the compilation by Exner (1978) and are shown in Tables 5 and 6. The values for ortho substitution are not considered because of the mixing of electronic effects with steric effects. Kier and Hall (1983) have reported on elements of the first period. Values selected for this study were limited to those obtained by similar experimental methods (pK in water or 50/50 water/ethanol) and those with reliable experimental values. For most of the values used here, Exner listed an experimental error of 0.1 or less. In Tables 5 and 6, substituents 4, 8, 18, 19 have somewhat larger errors, but were included to broaden the types of substituents studied. The results of a multiple linear regression are as follows:

$$\sigma_p = 0.435E^{\sigma} + 0.409E^{\pi} - 0.504E^n - 0.122 \qquad (12)$$
$$r = 0.978, \ s = 0.081, \ F = 151, \ n = 25$$

$$\sigma_m = 0.372E^{\sigma} + 0.302E^{\pi} - 0.148E^n - 0.054 \qquad (13)$$
$$r = 0.956, \ s = 0.070, \ F = 74, \ n = 25$$

The three parameters are highly independent; r for the three pairwise correlations are 0.12 for E^{σ}, E^{π}; 0.19 for E^{σ}, E^n; and 0.41

TABLE 5. Hamment sigma para values and calculated substituent effect.

ID	Substituent	E^σ	E^π	E^n	σp Obs	σp Calc	Res
1	CH_3	0.00	0.00	0.00	-0.16	-0.12	-0.04
2	C_2H_5	0.00	0.00	0.00	-0.15	-0.12	-0.03
3	CH_2OH	0.21	0.00	0.00	0.01	-0.03	0.04
4	$CH_2C_6H_5$	0.06	0.00	0.00	-0.06	-0.10	0.04
5	CF_3	1.13	0.00	0.00	0.54	0.37	0.17
6	$CH{=}CH_2$	0.16	0.15	0.00	-0.08	0.01	-0.19
7	CHO	0.44	0.75	0.00	0.43	0.38	0.05
8	COOH	0.65	0.75	0.00	0.44	0.47	-0.03
9	$CONH_2$	0.52	0.75	0.00	0.31	0.41	-0.01
10	$COCH_3$	0.44	0.75	0.00	0.47	0.38	0.09
11	$COOCH_3$	0.65	0.75	0.00	0.46	0.47	-0.01
12	COC_6H_5	0.50	0.75	0.00	0.46	0.40	0.06
13	$CONHCH_3$	0.52	0.75	0.00	0.36	0.41	-0.05
14	C_6H_5	0.22	0.15	0.00	-0.01	0.04	-0.05
15	$C{\equiv}CH$	0.47	0.60	0.00	0.23	0.33	-0.10
16	CN	0.63	1.20	0.00	0.65	0.64	0.01
17	NH_2	0.30	0.00	1.50	-0.66	-0.75	0.09
18	$NHCOCH_2$	0.39	0.00	0.50	-0.09	-0.20	0.11
19	$NHCONH_2$	0.40	0.00	0.50	-0.24	-0.20	-0.04
20	NO_2	1.05	0.95	0.00	0.78	0.72	0.06
21	OH	0.83	0.00	1.00	-0.38	-0.26	-0.12
22	OCH_3	0.83	0.00	1.00	-0.28	-0.26	-0.02
23	OC_2H_5	0.83	0.00	1.00	-0.24	-0.26	0.02
24	$OCOCH_3$	0.91	0.00	0.00	0.31	0.27	0.04
25	F	1.50	0.00	0.50	0.15	0.28	-0.13

TABLE 6.   Hamment sigma meta values and calculated substituent effect.

ID	Substituent	E^{σ}	E^{π}	E^{n}	σm Obs	σm Calc	Res
1	CH_3	0.00	0.00	0.00	-0.95	-0.05	0.00
2	C_2H_5	0.00	0.00	0.00	-0.07	-0.05	-0.02
3	CH_2OH	0.21	0.00	0.00	0.01	0.02	-0.01
4	$CH_2C_6H_5$	0.06	0.00	0.00	-0.05	-0.03	-0.02
5	CF_3	1.13	0.00	0.00	0.43	0.37	0.06
6	$CH{=}CH_2$	0.16	0.15	0.00	0.08	0.05	0.03
7	CHO	0.44	0.75	0.00	0.36	0.34	0.02
8	COOH	0.65	0.75	0.00	0.35	0.41	-0.06
9	$CONH_2$	0.52	0.75	0.00	0.28	0.37	-0.09
10	$COCH_3$	0.44	0.75	0.00	0.36	0.34	0.02
11	$COOCH_3$	0.65	0.75	0.00	0.35	0.41	-0.06
12	COC_6H_5	0.50	0.75	0.00	0.36	0.36	0.00
13	$CONHCH_3$	0.52	0.75	0.00	0.35	0.37	-0.02
14	C_6H_5	0.22	0.15	0.00	0.06	0.07	-0.01
15	$C{\equiv}CH$	0.47	0.60	0.00	0.20	0.30	-0.10
16	CN	0.63	1.20	0.00	0.61	0.54	0.07
17	NH_2	0.30	0.00	1.50	-0.09	-0.16	0.07
18	$NHCOCH_3$	0.39	0.00	0.50	0.14	0.02	0.02
19	$NHCONH_2$	0.40	0.00	0.50	-0.03	0.02	-0.05
20	NO_2	1.05	0.95	0.00	0.74	0.62	0.12
21	OH	0.83	0.00	1.00	0.02	0.11	-0.09
22	OCH_3	0.83	0.00	1.00	0.10	0.11	-0.01
23	OC_2H_5	0.83	0.00	1.00	0.10	0.11	-0.01
24	$OCOCH_3$	0.91	0.00	0.00	0.39	0.28	0.11
25	F	1.50	0.00	0.50	0.34	0.43	-0.09

for E^π, E^n. The calculated values, σ_p and σ_m, are given in Tables 5 and 6 along with residuals. No residuals are greater than twice the regression standard deviation.

It should be pointed out that since the Kier/Hall valence state electronegativity of hydrogen is zero, the same as $C(sp^3)$, the predicted value for alkyl groups are identical. Since the experimental values lie very close together, this may be an acceptable result. Exner (1978) has discussed both sides of this issue.

A point of discussion centers on triple-bonded groups such as the acetyleno- and cyano- groups. The electron withdrawing ability of these groups is greater than expected for the interaction of only that part of the pi system which directly overlaps the ring. The whole triple bonded pi system acts as an electron sink in such cases. Electron density flows into the pi system from the ring through the orbitals which overlap the ring. Electron density also accumulates in the pi system which is formally coplanar with the ring. To approximate this effect the, E^π contribution, eqn. (7) is doubled.

Two substituents with significant conformational dependence are not included in the correlation analysis. These substituents are $-N=CHC_6H_5$ and $-N=NC_6H_5$. Conformations can be tentatively assigned on the basis of molecular orbital studies. The imino substituent is oriented with respect to the ring so that the nitrogen lone pair can overlap with the ring, whereas in the other case the pi-N=N- system overlaps the benzene ring. Using these models and eqns. (12) and (13), it is possible to estimate the σ_p and σ_m values as follows for $-N=CHC_6H_5$:

Calculated $\sigma_p = -0.52$ Experimental $\sigma_p = -0.55$

Calculated $\sigma_m = -0.04$ Experimental $\sigma_m = -0.08$

and for $-N=NC_6H_5$:

Calculated $\sigma_p = -0.25$ Experimental $\sigma_p = -0.33$

Calculated $\sigma_m = -0.26$ Experimental $\sigma_m = -0.29$

The agreement with the experimental values is gratifying.

These results reveal for the first time a fairly successful effort to calculate Hammett sigma values directly from structure for a range of substituents. It cannot be claimed that this approach is a better method of estimating a numerical substituent effect on benzene or a replacement for the conventional experimental approach to these values. It can be stated that the work directly and logically links structure to this property, and that relative substituent effects can be calculated from this model. The work further reveals a very great significance for the counts of electrons, the δ and δ^V values, which also serve as the basic elements in the calculation of molecular connectivity indexes. This finding reinforces the belief in the rich information content residing in valence molecular connectivity indexes.

6. Quantitation of Solvent Polarity Based on Molecular Structure

A. Solvent Polarity

The term "solvent polarity" is widely used by chemists to characterize the observed manifestations of intermolecular interactions in a solution process. The processes may be chromatography, dissolution, or chemical reactions. The manifestations of the interactions are recorded as the separation or retention on stationary phases, the solubility, and the partitioning or reaction course and rate. Solvent polarity is a comparative term which the chemist uses intuitively to rank commonly employed compounds. This intuition, based on experience, permits the generalization that hydrocarbons are less polar than esters, while alcohols are more polar than esters of the same molecular weight.

B. Derivation of a Solvent Polarity Index from Molecular Structure

The solvent characteristics of a molecule depend on intermolecular interactions which, in turn, are dependent on structure. The generalization can be made that molecules classified as nonpolar according to any of the reported methods are molecules that possess few, if any, polar groups or bonds. Nonpolar molecules are distinguished by the absence of unsaturation or lone pair electrons. Pentane is universally regarded as nonpolar, having only C-H and C-C bonds which are devoid of electrons not axially directed between nuclei; while diethyl ether, with virtually the same molecular weight, is more polar, having two lone pairs of electrons on the oxygen atom. Similar comparisons between hexane and pentanol, cyclohexane and benzene, and isopentane and methyl acetate present cases of about the same molecular weight where molecules with pi and lone pair electrons are more polar than those without them. This observation is not surprising since lone pair electrons create significant dipoles capable of intermolecular interactions associated with polar solvents. The task then is to encode this structural information into a molecular index that will quantify solvent polarity from a purely structural basis.

The non-sigma electrons on atoms in a molecule enumerated by $\delta^v - \delta$ are encoded in $^1X - {}^1X^v$. The subtraction of chi indexes is reversed from the delta values since the reciprocal of the delta values is used in computing the molecular connectivity indexes. The effect on the calculated values of $^1X - {}^1X^v$ due to an increase of non-sigma electrons in a series of molecules is illustrated in Table 3. With increasing numbers of non-sigma electrons in molecules in this series in which ^1X is constant, the values of $^1X^v$ decrease; hence, $^1X - {}^1X^v$ increases down the list. In this series, the $^1X - {}^1X^v$ values also increase as the molecules increase in polarity. For molecules in an homologous series, such as the n-alkanols, the solvent polarity decreases with increasing size; however, the values of $^1X - {}^1X^v$ obviously remain constant. If $^1X - {}^1X^v$ is to reflect solvent polarity, the expression must be modified by a term describing increasing molecular weight. This can be accomplished by decreasing the value of $^1X - {}^1X^v$ by ^1X, which increases with size in an homologous series.

An index reflecting polarity may be written:

$$\text{polarity} = {}^1X - {}^1X^V - {}^1X = - {}^1X^V \tag{14}$$

To restate this relationship, it is proposed that solvent polarity is inversely related to ${}^1X^V$. Table 7 shows the calculated values of ${}^1X^V$ for some common solvents. Also included are other experimentally derived polarity indexes, $e^o(Al_2O_3)$, delta, and P', as well as the octanol-water partition coefficient.

C. Functional Group Number Weighting

A number of molecules in Table 7, such as ethylene glycol and dioxane, possess two isolated functional groups. These solvents are known to be more polar than their monofunctional counterparts of about equal molecular weight, propanol and pyran. The two functional groups may be regarded as having twice the opportunity or probability of engaging in dipolar or electron donor-acceptor interactions with a solute.

For purposes of defining this solvent polarity index, a functional group is defined as an ensemble of atoms with non-sigma electrons that engage, as a unit, in essentially a single type of intermolecular interaction. Thus, the two oxygens and the carbon atom of an ester group constitute a functional group in this definition. Similarly, the three atoms of a nitro group represent one functional group in nitrobenzene. The six carbon π electrons of the benzene ring also constitute a discrete functional group that acts separately from the nitro group. Thus, nitrobenzene is regarded as having two functional groups. A nitrogen atom in pyridine participates in the π-electron annulus which contributes to van der Waal's interactions. The nitrogen also may participate in bonding through the lone pair electrons. Therefore, pyridine has two functional groups by this definition.

TABLE 7.   Ranking of solvent polarity using $^1X^v/f$ index.

Molecule	$^1X^v/f$	a) p'	b) Delta	c) $^o(Al_2O_3)$	d) log p
Hexane	2.914	0.0	7.3	0.01	–
Chlorobenzene	2.508	2.7	9.6	0.30	2.46
Toluene	2.411	2.3	8.9	0.29	2.80
Carbon tetrachloride	2.390	1.7	8.6	0.18	2.72
Ethylene dichloride	2.190	3.7	9.7	0.49	1.48
Tetrahydrofuran	2.077	4.2	9.1	0.45	0.73
Chloroform	2.070	4.4	9.1	0.40	1.97
Butanol	2.023	3.9	11.3	–	0.88
Benzene	2.000	3.0	9.2	0.32	2.13
Ether	1.992	2.9	7.6	0.38	0.80
Ethyl acetate	1.904	4.3	8.6	0.58	0.70
Methyl ethyl ketone	1.765	4.5	9.3	0.51	0.27
Propanol	1.523	3.9	10.2	0.82	0.30
Dimethylformamide	1.388	–	11.5	–	-1.01
Nitrobenzene	1.250	4.5	11.1	–	1.85
Acetone	1.204	5.4	9.4	0.56	0.24
Benzonitrile	1.192	4.6	10.7	–	1.56
α-Picoline	1.135	4.8	–	–	–
Dioxane	1.073	4.8	9.8	0.56	-0.35
Ethanol	1.023	5.2	11.2	0.88	-0.30
Pyridine	0.925	5.3	10.4	0.71	0.65
Ethanolamine	0.678	–	13.5	–	-1.31
Ethylene glycol	0.566	5.4	13.5	1.11	-1.93
Methanol	0.447	6.6	12.9	0.95	-0.65
Water	0.0	9.0	21.0	–	-1.38

a) (Rohrschneider, 1968)   c) (Snyder, 1968)

b) (Hildebrand and Scott, 1964)   d) (Leo and Hansch, 1979)

To account for the effect of multiple interaction sites, it was proposed that the calculated $^1X^V$ value be divided by a factor, f, describing the number of discrete, isolated functional groups. This method was applied to nitrobenzene, benzonitrile, α-picoline, dioxane, pyridine, methoxyethanol, ethanolamine, and ethylene glycol.

The exception to this rule is the case in which one or more halogen atoms are present on different carbon atoms, i.e., ethylene dichloride. Chlorine does not make a significant contribution to a molecule in terms of enhancing its solvent polarity. Aryl and alkyl halides are classified among the more nonpolar solvents, i.e., carbon tetrachloride, chlorobenzenes, etc. Therefore, the value of $^1X^V$ computed for a halogen-containing molecule would be used unmodified.

Table 7 lists 26 of the more common solvents, ranked according to increasing solvent polarity computed as a diminishing value of $^1X^V/f$. This polarity index, based solely on molecular structure, is compared with the experimental polarity indexes derived by several methods.

Several observations emerge from comparisons of these indexes. The diminishing value of $^1X^V/f$, associated with increasing solvent polarity, parallels the increase in the values of P', delta, and $e^o(Al_2O_3)$, with the P' values being perhaps the best correlated. Each of these experimentally derived polarity indexes is based on a different method; thus, a very close correlation is not expected among them or with $^1X^V/f$. Nevertheless, for a broad definition of solvent polarity, $^1X^V/f$ performs quite well in comparison. The distinct advantage of using $^1X^V/f$ as a solvent polarity index is the fact that it is based exclusively on structure; therefore, it can be computed quickly and simply for any molecule, including those that may not be available.

The aqueous solubilities of these same molecules correlate fairly well with $^1X^V/f$. The aqueous solubility is minimal for molecules with $^1X^V/f$ values above 2.0, intermediate for $^1X^V/f$ values of 1.5-2.0, and miscible for practically all molecules with $^1X^V/f$ values less than 1.5. There are exceptions to these observations, but generally the calculated $^1X^V/f$ index ranks the molecules according to solvent polarity as well as any of the experimental indexes, the advantage clearly being in the purely structural basis for the calculation.

Another application of the $^1X^V/f$ solvent polarity index is obvious when binary solvent mixtures are considered. If it is assumed that when two nonreacting solvents are mixed the solvent polarity is some weighted average of their polarities, then it should be possible to estimate the solvent polarity of any mixture or, conversely, to design a solvent mixture with a specific solvent polarity. This latter course is often desirable when one solvent may possess unfavorable physical, chemical, or toxicological properties. As an example, ether may have optimum solvent polarity for a particular application; however, its volatility and flammability preclude its use from safety considerations. It is desirable to reproduce approximately the $^1X^V/f = 1.992$ ether polarity with a mixture of two solvents. Calculations show that an approximate 1:1 mixture of toluene and propanol has a $^1X^V/f$ value of 1.967, while a 2:1 mixture of methyl ethyl ketone and chlorobenzene has a $^1X^V/f$ value of 1.973.

Other applications of the index include its use as the basis of selection of a relatively nonpolar solvent that is heavier or lighter or miscible with water and having about the same polarity. Chloroform, butanol, and tetrahydrofuran, respectively, meet these specific criteria.

Finally, the index may prove useful in estimating the polarity of a molecule not commonly considered as a solvent or perhaps a polymeric structure such as the polyethers. As an example, the $^1X^V/f$ values lead to polarity rankings for some additional liquids: methylformamide, 1.024; diethylene glycol, 0.737; dimethoxy polyethylene glycol, $^1X^V/f$ approaches a limit of 1.10 with increasing size; morpholine, 1.142; various fluorinated ethanols, 0.0-0.5; glycerol, 0.569; and aniline, 1.100.

7. A Benzene-like or Aromaticity Index from Chi

A. Aromaticity and Benzene-Likeness

The attribution of "aromatic" in organic chemistry is a familiar concept in the classification of molecules with certain structural characteristics. The concept, as it is commonly understood, provides some basis for intuition concerning the chemical and physical properties of these molecules. In spite of this, aromaticity cannot be unequivocally demonstrated as a physico-chemical phenomenon. In this sense, it is like other useful characteristics such as electronegativity, branching, and polarity, which the chemist uses to interpret phenomena, describe structure, or to convey information.

The definitions, significance, and demonstration of aromaticity have been reviewed in a book by Lewis and Peters (1975). The central theme that emerges from all of the experimental and theoretical evidence is that benzene plays a unique role in any definition. Indeed, benzene is the prototypical example of the aromatic molecule and is often the reference standard against which other molecules are compared. This is true because of the unique pattern of structural characteristics in benzene. The carbon atoms are each in an sp^2 hybrid state, bond angles are identical and unstrained, all pi electrons participate equally in delocalized pi orbitals forming a cyclic continuum and all bonds of the same kind are of equal length. These observations plus a thorough analysis of all definitions has led Lewis and Peters (1975) to adopt the definition of aromatic as "having an electron organization like that of benzene". If we accept this definition of aromaticity as a starting point, it may be possible to achieve some approximate quantitation or ranking of molecules which are aromatic but which possess less of this characteristic than benzene. The practical value of such a ranking lies in its ability to anticipate some chemical properties, stability or potential for interaction with other molecules.

B.   Derivation of an Index of Benzene-Likeness

An approach to an index of benzene likeness begins with certain stated criteria. It is assumed that the molecule to be indexed is planar and cyclic since it is hard to imagine a non-cyclic molecule exhibiting many of the characteristics associated with benzene. The second criterion is that each atom in the ring participates in a delocalized bond with only its neighboring ring atoms. This insures the presence of an overlapping orbital continuum, orthogonal to the sigma bond framework and possessing no beginning or end. Finally we consider only neutral molecules in their ground state and confine our attention to five and six membered rings or fused ring systems formed from them.

A quantitation of benzene-likeness begins with a numerical coding of the atoms in the ring. We have shown that δ and δ^V associated with the valence state of an atom encode information about the number of sigma bonding electrons, the number of non-sigma electrons, the hybrid state, the relative atomic volume and the electronegativity. These delta values have been shown in eqn. (1) to correlate closely with valence state electronegativity within a periodic row. The direct interpretation of this expression is that the count of the number of pi and lone pair electrons on an atom ranks the atom according to its electronegativity.

These characteristics, particularly the uniformity of electro-negativity around a ring, or the deviation from it, must certainly have an influence on the physical and chemical properties of a cyclic molecule which we are considering. Thus, benzene is described by a uniform set of δ and δ^V values for each ring atom ($\delta = 2$, $\delta^V = 3$). In contrast, pyridine is described by five sets of delta values ($\delta = 2$, $\delta^V = 3$) and a unique set of delta values for the nitrogen atom ($\delta = 2$, $\delta^V = 5$). It is expected that this deviation from uniformity relative to benzene, contributes to the perceived difference in properties leading to the notion that pyridine is probably less aromatic than benzene. The two additional lone pair electrons and one less hydrogen atom on nitrogen, encoded in

$\delta^V = 5$, compared to a ·benzene carbon, $\delta^V = 3$, constitutes a numerical basis for comparing or ranking the two molecules and interpreting this as a criterion of aromaticity or benzene-likeness.

The next step in the development of an index is the translation of individual atom delta values in a given molecule into a single number encoding information about the electronic structure and its difference from benzene. When $\delta^V = \delta$ for an atom, there are no pi or lone pair electrons on the atom. This case does not appear under the stated criteria since such an atom would not contribute to the delocalized portion of the molecule. When $\delta^V > \delta$, the number of pi and lone pair electrons in a molecule is encoded into the difference between ^1X and $^1X^V$. In the case of benzene, $^1X = 3.000$ and $^1X^V = 2.000$. The difference, $^1X - {}^1X^V = 1.000$, reflects the information that there are six pi electrons contributed by six atoms in the ring. In the case of pyridine, $^1X = 3.000$ and $^1X^V = 1.850$; hence, $^1X - {}^1X^V = 1.150$. This is higher than the value of 1.000 calculated for benzene due to the replacement of a carbon atom with an atom with a higher δ^V value (nitrogen) in the case of pyridine. This difference reflects the change in structure or relative benzene-likeness of pyridine.

The comparison can be simplified by realizing that ^1X has a constant value, 3.000, for all six-membered rings. Thus $^1X^V$ values alone encode the structural differences among six-membered rings with the stated criteria. A direct comparison can be made between two rings of differing numbers of atoms (bonds) by comparing $^1X^V$ values per bond. Let b represent the number of bonds. From the value $^1X^V/b$, we derive an index of benzene-likeness, B:

$$B = (^1X^V/b)/[^1X^V/b(\text{benzene})] = 3{}^1X^V/b \qquad (15)$$

The indole molecule illustrates the calculation.

$$^1X^V \ (\text{indole}) = 4(3 \cdot 3)^{-0.5} + 4(3 \cdot 4)^{-0.5} + 2(4 \cdot 4)^{-0.5} = 2.988$$
$$B = 3{}^1X^V/10 = 0.90$$

A second example is 1,2,4-oxadiazole:

$$^1\chi^v \text{ (oxadiazole)} = 3(3 \cdot 5)^{-0.5} + (3 \cdot 6)^{0.5} + (5 \cdot 6)^{-0.5} = 1.194$$
$$B = 3^1\chi^v/5 = 0.72$$

A third case illustrates the calculation of a substituted ring using o-xylene as an example:

$$^1\chi^v \text{(xylene)} = 3(3 \cdot 3)^{-0.5} + (4 \cdot 4)^{-0.5} = 1.827$$
$$B = 3^1\chi^v/6 = 0.91$$

C. B Values of Heterocycles

An interesting application of the B index calculations is the consideration of heterocycles. Molecules with a variety of ring size, heteroatom content and number are calculated in Table 8. An initial test of the B values is the calculated ordering benzene > thiophene > pyrrole > furan. Compared with the consensus of ranking by aromaticity, pyridine is ranked between pyrrole and furan although it is sometimes equated with benzene. The B value calculated for pyridine may be interpreted as reflecting the lower electrophilic reactivity due to the basic lone pair of electrons influencing substitution reactions using Lewis acids.

The resonance energies per bond calculated by the Klages (1949) method, shown in Table 8, agree precisely with the B value order: benzene > thiophene > pyrrole > pyridine > furan. The A values of Julg (1967), based on bond length variation, agree with this ranking except for pyridine. Likewise, diamagnetic susceptibility exaltation is found to parallel the ranking of a number of molecules except for pyridine. This same property ranks other heterocycles in parallel with B values although 1,3-oxazole has a Λ value somewhat higher than predicted from the low B value. The calculated total binding energy, E, (Roche 1979), ranks the ten molecules for which data are available quite closely with the calculated B values. Finally, in

TABLE 8.   B index for monocyclic heterocycles.

Molecule	B	a) RE/b	b) A	c) Λ	d) E	e) non-loc
Benzene	1.00	6.00	1.00	13.7		-39
Thiophene	.97	5.74	0.93	13.0		
Pyrrole	.95	4.24	0.91	10.2	20.62	
Pyridine	.93	3.83	1.00	13.4		-28
Furan	.88	3.16	0.87	8.9		
1,3-Thiazole	.88			12.3		
Pyrazole	.86			6.6	13.23	
Pyridazine	.86			7.1		-27
Imidazole	.86				12.23	
Pyrimidine	.85					-18
Pyrazine	.85			7.1		-26
1,2-Oxazole	.81					
1,3,4-Thiadiazole	.80			5.1		
1,3-Oxazole	.79			8.2		
1,2,3-Triazole	.78				6.35	
1,2,5-Triazole	.78				6.65	
1,3,4-Triazole	.78				4.62	
1,3,5-Triazine	.77					-12
1,2,4-Triazole	.77				5.02	
1,2,3,5-Tetrazole	.70				-0.88	
1,2,3,4-Tetrazole	.70				-0.88	
Sydnone	.68					
Pentazole	.63					-6

a) Resonance energy, Kcal/mole/bond (Klages, 1949).
b) Aromaticity index of Julg and Francois (1967).
c) Diamagnetic susceptibility exaltation (Dauben, et. al., 1971).
d) Calculated total binding energy, eV (Roche and Pujol, 1971).
e) Non-local magnetisabilities, (Battaglia and Ritchie, 1977).

Table 8 the B values of six heterocycles correspond rather well with the non-local magnetizabilities of Battaglia and Ritchie (1977).

From the B value of heterocycles in Table 8, it can be concluded that aromaticity or benzene-likeness decreases with an increasing number of heteroatoms. Sulfur in the ring has less of a diminishing effect on B than does nitrogen while an oxygen in the ring reduces the B value to the greatest extent. This is confirmed by comparison with the various indexes in Table 8.

D. General Comments

The numerical value of the benzene-likeness index, B, is derived from a quantitation of the extent of branching of the ring or rings, the number of rings and their relationship to each other, and the heteroatom number and type. All of these attributes influence physical and chemical properties giving rise to experimental and theoretical values which deviate from benzene as a reference molecule. This is the essence of the notion of aromaticity or, as it has been described, benzene-likeness.

The non-empirical nature of the B values, based on electron counts in valence state atoms, makes it a simple method for the approximation of structural similarity to benzene. This, in turn, presents a convenient approach to the estimation of chemical and physical characteristics of selected cyclic molecules.

8. $^mX - {}^mX^V$ Index for Atom-Specific Properties

A. The Information in $^mX - {}^mX^V$

We have demonstrated that $^1X - {}^1X^V$ is an index encoding information about non-sigma electrons on an atom. It is apparent that $^0X - {}^0X^V$ encodes information about just non-sigma electrons on an atom irrespective of the topological environment of the atom which has $\delta^V = \delta$. It follows that $^1X - {}^1X^V$ carries similar information but would include the branching pattern of all atoms adjacent to the atom in which $\delta^V = \delta$. Thus, $^1X - {}^1X^V$ describes the influence of the atoms on a heteroatom or double bond. Finally, the index $^2X - {}^2X^V$ would describe the influence of all β atoms beta to the heteroatom.

This analysis makes it possible to consider certain chemical and physical properties which are primarily dependent on the structure of one atom or bond in a molecule. Examples include the acidity, ionization potential, and double bond reactivity. With one or more sets of chi differences, enough electronic information and neighboring group topology may be encoded to permit a close correlation with the magnitude of the property. One example serves to confirm this expectation.

B. Ionization Potential

The ionization potential of a molecule measures the energy of the loss of an electron from a molecule, particularly from an atom with pi or lone pair electrons. This property is a function of the nature of a particular atom and is influenced to some extent by the nature of atoms α and β to it. The indexes of the type $^mX - {}^mX^V$ carry both categories of information and can be used to closely correlate this property. For a combined list of amines, alcohols and ethers measured by Wantanabe et al (1962), the equations and statistics are:

$$IP(eV) = 5.513(^OX - {}^OX^V) + 6.595$$
$$r = 0.808, \ s = 0.578, \ n = 24, \ F = 41$$

$$IP(eV) = 5.014(^OX - {}^OX^V) + 5.166(^1X - {}^1X^V) + 5.341$$
$$r = 0.955, \ s = 0.299, \ n = 24, \ F = 109$$

$$IP(eV) = 5.364(^OX - {}^OX^V) + 6.341(^1X - {}^1X^V) + 1.517(^2X - {}^2X^V) + 4.253$$
$$r = 0.993, \ s = 0.123, \ n = 24, \ F = 461$$

The equations successfully model the contribution of the hetereoatom and adjacent atom inductive effects on the IP. From the three variable equation it can be concluded that the influence of the α atom on the ionization potential is over four times that of the β atom. This is consistent with our understanding of the inductive effect of substituents on heteroatoms.

9. Summary

The information resident in molecular connectivity indexes has been demonstrated in a variety of examples. From the derivation of δ and δ^V, the counts of sigma, pi and lone pair electrons are incorporated into the $^m X_t^V$ and $^m X_t$ indexes. By selection of the appropriate indexes, it is possible to encode certain elements of electronic structure influencing physical and biological properties. More examples are described in Chapter 7.

References

Battaglia, M. and Ritchie, G. (1977). Kerr constants, Cotton-Mouton constants and magnetic anisotropies of pyridazine, pyrimidine and pyrazine. J. Chem. Soc. Perkin II, 897-900.

Dauben, H. J., Wilson, J. D. and Laity, J. L. (1971), in Nonbenzenoid Aromatics Vol. II. (Edited by J. P. Snyder). p. 167. Academic, New York.

Exner, O. in Correlation Analysis in Chemistry. (1978) (Edited by N. B. Chapman and J. Shorter). Plenum, New York.

Hildebrand, J. H. and Scott, R. L. (1964). The Solubility of Non-Electrolytes. Dover, New York.

Hinze, J. and Jaffe, H. H. (1962). Orbital electronegativity of neutral atoms. J. Am. Chem. Soc., 84, 540-546.

Hinze, J. and Jaffe, H. H. (1963). Orbital electronegativities of the periods three A and four A and of positive ions of periods one and two. J. Chem. Phys., 67, 1501-1505.

Huheey, J. E. (1965). The electronegativity of groups. J. Phys. Chem., 69, 3284-3291.

102

Huheey, J. E. (1965). Group electronegativity and polar substituent constants. J. Org. Chem. 31, 2365-2369.

Julg, A. and Francois, P. (1967). Research on the geometry of non-alternant hydrocarbons: the influence on the transition energies and a new definition of aromaticity. Theoret. Chim. Acta, 1, 249-259.

Kier, L. B. and Hall, L. H. (1976). Molecular Connectivity in Chemistry and Drug Research. Academic, New York.

Kier, L. B. and Hall, L. H. (1981). Derivation and significance of valence molecular connectivity. J. Pharm. Sci., 70, 583-589.

Kier, L. B. and Hall, L. H. (1983). Estimation of substituent group electronic influence from molecular connectivity delta values. Quant. Struct-Act. Relat. 2, 163-167.

Lewis, D. and Peters, D. (1975). Facts and Theories of Aromaticity. MacMillan, London.

Mulliken, R. S. (1934). A new electronegativity scale. J. Chem. Phys. 2, 782-793.

Pauling, L. (1932). The energy of single bonds and the relative electronegativity of atoms. J. Am. Chem. Soc. 54, 3570-3582.

Roche, M. and Pujol, L. (1971). LCAO-SCF treatment applied to nitrogen. J. Chim. Phys., 68, 465-470.

Rohrschneider, L. (1968). Advances in Chromatography. Vol. IV. Dekker, New York.

Sanderson, R. T. (1954). Electronegativities in inorganic chemistry. J. Chem. Ed. 31, 2-7.

Sanderson, R. T. (1976). Chemical Bonds and Bond Energy. Academic, New York.

Snyder, L. R. (1968). Principles of Adsorption Chromatography. Dekker, New York.

Wantanabe, K., Nakayama, T. and Mottl, J. (1962). Ionization potentials of some molecules. J. Quant. Spectrosc. Radiat. Transfer. 2, 369-382.

CHAPTER 5
Statistical Considerations

1. Introduction

The common basis of QSAR studies is the analysis of a data set which consists of a list of compounds with their molecular structures and biological activities. Analysis of the data may be done in terms of a model which has been proposed to explain the behavior of the system under investigation. If the model is a complete mechanistic representation of the system at the level of the structures of all components, then direct calculation of the measured effect may be possible. This approach is the most common method used in physical chemistry and closely related areas, but is rarely the case in biological studies.

QSAR is essentially the search for a model which correlates activity to independent variables. For this reason, analysis in QSAR is statistical in nature. Any developed relationships or classifications are stated in terms of probability. This chapter focuses on measures of the quality of QSAR models.

The finding of a satisfactory relationship between activity and measures of structure does not confirm or prove the actuality of such a model. One cannot logically say that the finding of a good relationship demonstrates the operation of a particular model. The possibility exists that another model may produce equally satisfactory statistics. Statistical methods lead to QSAR models which must be held tentatively.

It is useful at this point to present some statistical background for the application of molecular connectivity to problems in QSAR. These remarks are brief and presented without proof and derivation.

There are many excellent sources for these topics and some are listed here for convenience. Of particular interest are books by Bard (1974), Bevington (1969), Daniel and Wood (1980), Draper and Smith (1981), Freund and Littel (1981), Neter and Wasserman (1974), Overall and Klett (1972) and Rao (1973).

2. Statistical Background

A. Basic Terms and Definitions

The usual quantities of statistical interest and the commonly used symbols are introduced in the following summary and discussion.

Terms, Definitions and Relations

n: number of observations in a data set

x_i: individual observation on quantity x

μ : population average

σ : population standard deviation

$\bar{x}$: sample average

$$\bar{x} = \Sigma\ x/n \quad \text{(note: } \Sigma\ x \text{ means } \sum_{i=1}^{n} x_i\text{)}$$

d_i: deviation of individual observation from the mean, sometimes called the error, e_i

$$e_i = d_i = x_i - \bar{x}$$

SSE: sum of the squares of the deviations (or errors), often called simply the sum of squares, SS

$$SS = SSE = \Sigma\ (x_i - \bar{x})^2 = \Sigma\ d_i^{\,2}$$

DF: degrees of freedom, the number of independent pieces of information remaining after quantities have been calculated

DF = n-1   for variance in simple average
DF = n-2   for simple linear least squares
DF = n-m-1 for procedure which determines m parameters

MS: mean square sum

$$MS = SS/DF$$

s^2: sample variance, var, equal to mean square sum

$$s^2 = \Sigma (x_i - \bar{x})^2/(n-1)$$

s: sample standard deviation, equal to the square root of the sample variance.

The mean is the sample estimate of the average or centroid of the population of x values. If the distribution is normal, the values of x are distributed about the mean according to the Gaussian function. In a normal distribution the sum of deviations is zero.

$$\Sigma d_i = \Sigma (x_i - \bar{x}) = 0$$

In other words, the set of x_i values and the mean are not independent.

The degrees of freedom associated with the sum of x values is the number of independent values. In the computation of the variance, the mean is used. The degrees of freedom associated with the variance (and the sum of squares) is n-1.

It is useful to have a measure of the spread of values in the same units as the x values. The standard deviation is just the square root of the variance and is on the same scale as x.

An analysis of variance, called ANOVA, provides the investigator with the quantities necessary to evaluate the data set. Consider, as a specific example, several sets of determinations of the quantity x, say, m sets of n data points each. In general, the means of these sets will not be identical. The question arises, then, whether each of these m sets of observations comes from the same population. The question may be approached as follows.

A basic theorem in statistics states that the sum of squares for the total data set, SST, may be written as a sum of two terms: SSW, sum of squares within groups; and SSA, sum of squares among groups,

$$SST = SSA + SSW$$
$$\Sigma (\bar{x}_T - x)^2 = \Sigma (\bar{x}_T - \bar{x}_G)^2 + \Sigma (\bar{x}_G - x)^2$$

where $\bar{x}_G$ is the mean of a group and $\bar{x}_T$ is the mean of all data.

One can now test the hypothesis that each data set (group, sample) comes from the same population by comparing the variance among groups with the variance within groups. The variance ratio or F test is used; it is based on the mean square variance.

$$F_{1,n} = MSA/MSW$$

The mean square error (MS) is simply the sum of squares (SS) divided by the appropriate degrees of freedom (DF).

$$MSA = SSA/(m-1) = \Sigma (\bar{x}_T - \bar{x}_G)^2/(m-1)$$
$$MSW = SSW/m(n-1) = \Sigma (\bar{x}_G - x)^2/m(n-1)$$

The F value, associated with the two numbers, 1, for one mean, and n, for the number of observations, can be compared to tabulated values for random samples taken from normal distributions. If the computed value of F is less than the tabulated value, then one can state that the sample came from the same population at a confidence level depending on that used in the table. A 95% confidence level is commonly used in QSAR work. The general proposition of hypothesis testing may be examined in detail in appropriate sources. The quantities introduced here, however, will be employed in the discussions of statistical methods used in the QSAR of molecular connectivity.

B. Linear Models

A standard approach in QSAR studies is the development of a simple linear relationship between the biological activity and a measure of the structure of the molecules in the data set. The actual equation used may be developed on a theoretical basis or may have been previously developed empirically.

Measures of activity are commonly expressed in terms of a molar concentration. In the typical dose-response curve, the logarithm of the dose is assumed to be linearly related to the biological response. The activity measure is the log of molar concentration to effect a certain level of response, usually 50% of maximum. Since the typical molarity values are less than one molar, the log values are negative. For this reason the activity measure is usually negated to produce a measure of activity which is positive:

$$pC = -\log c = \log 1/c$$

This is analogous to the definition of pH. On this scale, greater potency (smaller concentration to effect response) is related directly to greater pC.

For this discussion let the variable x stand for the measure of molecular structure which serves as the independent variable in QSAR. The activity will be represented as y; hence, the linear model is written as:

$$pC = y = b_0' + b_1'x \tag{1}$$

The coefficients b_0' and b_1' are also called the intercept and slope, respectively. This equation states that there is a linear relationship between the dependent variable y (pC) and the independent variable x. This relation is an exact mathematical relation; however, when actual experimental values are used, there is not an exact relationship between x and y because of included errors, e_i:

$$y_i = b_0 + b_1 x_i + e_i \qquad (2)$$

The coefficients b_0 and b_1 are estimates of the actual model parameters b_0' and b_1'. These estimates are to be determined by statistical methods from the experimental set of y_i values and the set of values for structure variable x_i. The reasons for the inexactitude in eqn. (2) is that it includes experimental errors in y_i, error in the statistical estimation of the parameters (b_0 and b_1), and the possibility that the linear model (eqn. 2) is not entirely appropriate for some (or all) of the data. Thus, the estimates of the equation coefficients or parameters are influenced by all of these sources of error.

C. Least Squares Analysis of Simple Linear Cases

The most commonly used method for obtaining parameter estimates b_i is the least squares method of regression analysis, or least squares for short. For this discussion consider the data in Table 1 and the plot in Figure 1. This data set was reported by Ickikawa and Yamano (1967) on the conversion of cytochrome P-450 to P-420 in rat liver. The set consists of 14 phenols. Along with the name is the measure of activity (Act) which is the log molar concentration for 50% conversion, pEC_{50}. The independent variable is the $^1X^V$ or first order valence chi index. Calc and Res will be defined later.

Figure 1 shows a plot of activity (y) versus $^1X^V$ (x), sometimes called a scatter plot. Often, the general features of the relationship (or lack thereof) are revealed in such a plot. Nonlinearity,

TABLE 1. Data table for the conversion of cytochrome P-450 to
P-420 by phenols in rat liver.

Obs	Compound	$^1X^v$	a) Act	b) Calc	Res
1	Phenol	2.134	1.07	0.92	0.15
2	2-Iodo-	3.319	2.09	1.99	0.10
3	2-Chloro-	2.618	1.60	1.36	0.24
4	3-Hydroxy-	2.269	0.81	1.04	-0.23
5	3-Methyl-	2.545	1.50	1.29	0.21
6	3-Ethyl-	3.106	1.82	1.80	0.02
7	3-Amino-	2.334	0.46	1.10	-0.64
8	4-Methyl-	2.545	1.48	1.29	0.19
9	4-Carboxy-	2.723	1.15	1.46	-0.31
10	4-Bromo-	3.027	2.04	1.73	0.31
11	2,4-Dichloro-	3.183	2.11	1.87	0.24
12	2,4,6-Trichloro-	3.579	2.21	2.23	-0.02
13	2,3,4,6-Tetrachloro-	4.069	2.65	2.67	-0.02
14	Pentachloro-	4.558	2.90	3.12	-0.22

a) pEC_{50} from Ichikawa and Yamano (1967)
b) Calculated from eqn. (7.)

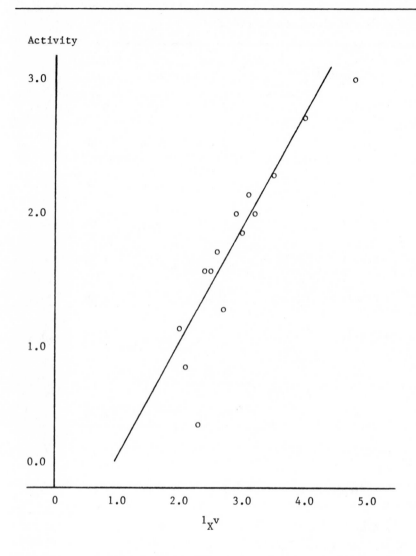

FIGURE 1. A plot of the biological activity, log of molar concentration for 50% conversion of cytochrome P-450 to P-420, versus the first order valence connectivity index. The straight line is the computed regression line based on a linear model with the first order valence chi index.

potential outliers, and data entry errors may be revealed. The importance of this first step cannot be overemphasized. As Wood and Daniel (1980) put it, "Festina lente" (quoting Caesar): "Make haste slowly." Begin the analysis with a careful review of the data set. The basis of selection of $^1x^v$ as the independent variable will be discussed later. For the present we consider how the "best" estimates of the linear parameters b_i' can be obtained (as b_i) from eqn. (2). An important consideration in the evaluation of the adequacy of eqn. (2) for a given data set is the agreement between y values calculated from eqn. (2) and the experimental values of y. The difference between these two is called the residual, res_i.

$$res_i = y_i(obs) - y_i(calc)$$

In keeping with earlier discussion, the sum of the squares of the residuals will be examined. It is usually called the residual sum of squares, RSS, or the sum squared error, SSE.

$$SSE = RSS = \Sigma\, res_i^2 = \Sigma\, [y_i(obs) - y_i(calc)]^2 \tag{3}$$

On the basis of certain statistical arguments, the best estimates of the parameters are determined by minimizing RSS (Bevington, 1969). RSS can be considered as a function of the estimate parameters b_0 and b_1. The least squares solution is to find the values of b_0 and b_1 for which RSS is a minimum, a standard problem for calculus. The function is at a minimum when the first derivatives (with respect to b_0 and b_1) are zero.

Eqn. (3) can be restated in terms of b_0 and b_1:

$$RSS = \Sigma\, (y_i - b_0 - b_1x_i)^2 \tag{4}$$

Finding the minimum leads to two equations with the model parameters b_0 and b_1 as the unknowns. The solution to these two simultaneous equations leads to the least squares estimates for the parameters:

$$b_1 = (x_i - \bar{x})(y_i - \bar{y})/(x_i - \bar{x})^2 \qquad (5a)$$

$$b_1 = (n\, x_i^2\, y_i - x_i\, x_i y_i)/[n\, x_i^2 - (x_i)^2)] \qquad (5b)$$

$$b_0 = \bar{y} - b_1 \bar{x} \qquad (6)$$

For b_1, eqn. (5a) is better for statistical insight while eqn. (5b) is better for computation. These equations show that b_1 is the ratio of the covariance of y and x to the variance in x. For b_0 (the intercept), only the average values of x and y are required. Also, note that $\bar{y} = b_0 + b_1 \bar{x}$ and that the fitted or calculated line passes through the point $y = \bar{y}$ and $x = \bar{x}$.

D. Results and Analysis

An important first step in the analysis of the results of the least squares procedure is to examine how closely the calculated regression line falls to the actual experimental data. The least squares parameters b_0 and b_1 are used to calculate activities according to the model equation,

$$y_i \text{ (calc)} = b_0 + b_1 x_i$$

The calculated values are given under the heading Calc in Table 1, and the regression equation is plotted as the line in Figure 1. The residuals are also given in Table 1 under Res.

An examination of the residuals shows generally good agreement. Most of the residual values are not large and the data points generally fall near the regression line. One residual, for observation no. 7, is much larger than the others and falls below the line. Another method of residual analysis is shown in Figure 2, a plot of the residuals against the observed activity. The large residual for no. 7 is clearly visible in the plot. If the data are truly randomly distributed with respect to the model equation, then the residuals should be randomly distributed about the zero line in Figure 2.

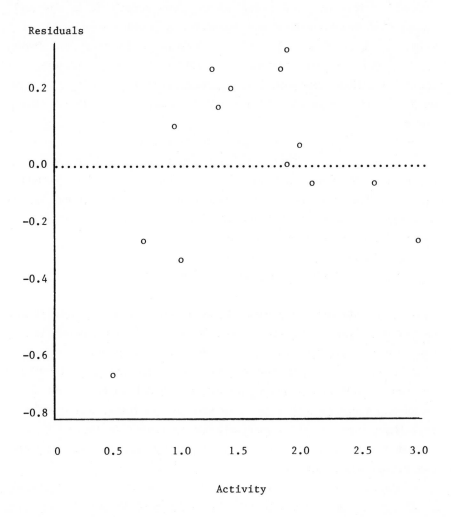

FIGURE 2. A plot of the residuals against the observed activity
in the cytochrome P-450 conversion regression based
only on the first order valence chi index.

This plot will reveal much when a poor fit is obtained. Analysis of residuals is a very useful tool in the development of a model. A good description of this analysis is in Wood and Daniel (1980). For the present it can be stated qualitatively that the least squares solution represented by Figures 1 and 2 is a good fit. The quality of the goodness of fit will be examined in the following sections.

An ANOVA table for regression analysis is given for the present data set in Table 2. The partitioned sum of squares is given in top left-hand side along with the corresponding degrees of freedom. The mean square values are the sum of squares term divided by the corresponding degrees of freedom. A useful statistic for comparison is the standard deviation of the fit,

$$s = \text{rms error} = (SSE/DF)^{\frac{1}{2}}$$

This is the standard deviation of the fitted values compared to the observed values of activity. The s value can be related to the experimental estimation of error. However, s includes sources of error related to experimental uncertainty plus error from the fitting process as well as any inadequacy in the model. Only for an exact model and for data with very small errors does the standard error of regression approach the typical experimental error in the data.

From the parameter estimates the equation representing the model can be written as follows:

$$pC = 0.905 \ (0.110) \ {}^{1}x^{V} - 1.008 \ (0.337) \tag{7}$$

The quantities in parentheses are the standard errors of the coefficients. From such standard errors the Student t value can be calculated as:

$$t_i = b_i \ / \ s(b_i)$$

Based on these t values and appropriate statistical tables one can compute confidence intervals for the coefficient and tests of

TABLE 2.   Regression results on the conversion of cytochrome P-450 to P-420 in rat liver by phenols using $^1x^v$.

ANALYSIS OF VARIANCE

Source	DF	Sum of Squares	Mean Square	F Value	Prob > F
Model	1	5.2526	5.2526	67.99	0.0001
Error	12	0.9271	0.0773		
Total	13	6.1797			

Standard Deviation	0.2780
R Squared	0.8500
Correlation Coefficient	0.9220

PARAMETER ESTIMATES

Variable	Parameter Estimate	Standard Error	t for HO: Parameter = 0	Prob > T
Intercept	-1.0080	0.3374	-2.987	0.0113
$^1x^v$	0.9046	0.1097	8.245	0.0001

significance can be applied to the coefficients. It can be determined whether the slope is significantly different from zero. The last column at the bottom of Table 2 states the probability that the slope is not significantly different from zero. For b_1, that probability is .0001; conversely, the probability is 99.9999% that b_1 is not zero.

If the slope is not significantly different from zero, the model should be stated with that coefficient equal to zero, $y = b_0$. In that case the best estimate for a predicted value of y is a constant, the same value for all observations. That estimate is simply the average y, $\bar{y}$, as shown by eqn. (6). In other words, the y values are just randomly distributed according to x, and one can do no better than estimate y as its average value when the slope is not different from zero.

Another common indicator of the quality of the least squares fit is the correlation coefficient. It is actually computed as the square directly from the analysis of variance terms. The quantity r^2 is the ratio of the sum squared error attributed to the model, SSM, to the total sum squared error, SST:

$$ r^2 = SSM/SST = \Sigma [y_i(calc) - \bar{y}\ ]^2\ /\ \Sigma [y_i(obs) - \bar{y}\ ]^2 $$

Using the relation on sums of squares,

$$ r^2 = SSM/SST = SSM/(SSM + RSS) = 1 - SSM/RSS $$

where RSS is the residual sum squared error. Thus, r^2 is the fraction of the overall variance in y which is accounted for by the model. Sometimes $100\ r^2$ is called the percent variance explained.

The correlation coefficient r lies between 0 and 1. The value of 1 means a perfect correlation; $r = 0$ means a totally random correlation. Actually, a set of n random pairs of numbers may not have a correlation $r = 0$. There is some finite, non-zero chance that a set of data may not be different from a random set. The F statistic, or variance ratio, may be used to assess the probability that the correlation is significantly different from random:

$$\text{Let} \quad DFR = (N-m-1)/m$$

$$F = DFR \cdot SSM/RSS = DFR \cdot r^2/(1-r^2)$$

where m is the number of variables. By consulting the appropriate tables, one can determine the level of significance of the correlation. In Table 2, the probability that r is not significant is given as $p < .0001$.

As pointed out earlier, observation no. 7 has a large residual; in fact, its residual is 2.3 times the standard deviation of the regression, 0.278. It lies well below the regression line, Figure 1. The data in Figure 1 have some appearance of being nonlinear and the residuals in Figure 2 tend to suggest the same feature. The suggestion that observation no. 7 may be an outlier can be evaluated in a straightforward statistical manner. It is possible to estimate confidence limits for the predicted value. Statistical programs will print out intervals as shown in Table 3 for the present data set.

Examination of Table 3 reveals that the observed experimental value for observation no. 7 lies on the lower limit of the 95% confidence interval. Perhaps this data set does warrant further investigation, especially observation no. 7. Since this examination will require consideration of nonlinear equations as well as those involving more than one independent variable, it will be useful to examine such cases generally. Before that question is addressed, let us consider the effect of deleting an outlier.

E. Deletion of an Outlier

For this data set, significant improvement is achieved by deleting no. 7, as shown by eqn. (8).

$$pC = 0.827 \; {}^1x^v - 0.720 \tag{8}$$

$$r = 0.949, \; s = 0.20, \; F = 100, \; n = 13$$

TABLE 3.   Predicted values and confidence limit intervals (95%)
for the cytochrome P-450 conversion regression using
only the first order valence chi index.

Obs	Measured Activity	Predicted Activity	Lower 95% Prediction Limit	Upper 95% Prediction Limit	Residual
1	1.07	0.923	0.263	1.583	0.147
2	2.09	1.994	1.363	2.626	0.096
3	1.60	1.360	0.727	1.994	0.240
4	0.81	1.044	0.393	0.695	-0.234
5	1.50	1.294	0.658	1.931	0.206
6	1.82	1.801	1.174	2.429	0.019
7	0.46	1.103	0.456	1.750	-0.643
8	1.48	1.294	0.658	1.931	0.186
9	1.15	1.455	0.826	2.085	-0.305
10	2.04	1.730	1.103	2.357	0.310
11	2.11	1.872	1.243	2.500	0.238
12	2.21	2.230	1.588	2.872	-0.020
13	2.65	2.673	1.996	3.350	-0.023
14	2.90	3.116	2.387	3.845	-0.22

Further, the coefficients have changed considerably from those in
eqn. (7), showing the influence of the one outlier, no. 7.   If it
could be established that there is something atypical about 3-amino
phenol, then eqn. (8) is a better representation of the model.   Such
a decision, however, cannot be made on purely statistical grounds.

3. Multiple Linear and Simple Nonlinear Cases

A. The General Situation

Often, the simple linear model represented as eqn. (1) is not appropriate for a specific problem, or is not statistically adequate for the data set. The actual system under consideration may require more than one independent variable or the relation to activity may not be linear.

Both of these cases may be handled with the following general multiple linear regression equation:

$$y_i = b_0 + b_1x_1 + b_2x_2 + \ldots + b_nx_n + e_i \qquad (9)$$

(It is understood that x_1 actually stands for x_{1i}; that is, the value of the first independent variable for the ith observation.)

Certain simple nonlinear cases may be handled in this fashion. The linear term x in the regression equation may be defined in terms of the actual independent variable x' in a nonlinear fashion, such as:

$$x = x'^2 \qquad \text{(quadratic or parabolic)} \qquad (10)$$

or

$$x = 1/x' \qquad \text{(reciprocal or hyperbolic)} \qquad (11)$$

These are two common cases encountered in QSAR. Consider the cited sources for further discussion and examples, especially Wood and Daniel (1980) and Bevington (1969). For our purposes, the discussion will be limited to eqns. (9) - (11). When there is more than one variable, there are additional quantities which may be calculated and used to gain insight into the statistical analysis of the regression equation. Only two modifications of the F test will be mentioned here. The regression analysis of an equation with n variables (x_1, x_2, ... x_n) may be done sequentially: first with x_1; then with x_1 and x_2; and finally on all n independent variables. If a variable contributes significantly to the regression, the measures of goodness of fit should improve with the addition of that variable. Specifically, the sum of squares attributed to the regression model should increase, becoming a larger fraction of the total sum of squares for the data set when a significant variable is added to the equation.

This improvement and its significance can be judged by the sequential F test, F_k for the addition of the kth variable.

$$F_k = \Delta SSM/RSS = [(r^2_k - r^2_{k-1})\ (n - k - 1)]\ /\ k$$

The number of variables in the larger equation is k. The increase in the sum squared error for the model is Δ SSM. F_k corresponds to the variance ratio for the addition of the kth (last) variable to the equation. One can consult F tables for 1 and n-k-1 degrees of freedom. If the table entry is less than F_k, then the addition of the variable is considered to have made a significant improvement.

A related test is the partial F test. It is computed in an analogous manner from data developed from the regression for each of the independent variables as if each were the last entered into the equation.

The earlier discussion suggested some possible specific deficiency in the model despite the overall goodness of fit. Attention was drawn to observation no. 7, to its large residual and to the nonrandom distribution of residuals. At least three possibilities come to mind:

i.   The problem may arise from one poor experimental data point no. 7. If this is the case or if no. 7, 3-aminophenol, is atypical of the data set, that observation should be left out. In this manner, the parameters are not influenced by an atypical compound or poor experimental value. (See section 2.E.).

ii.   A linear model may not be appropriate for the data set. This is one possible interpretation for the present data set. Based on theory concerning the problem at hand or based on experience with related problems, a nonlinear model should be examined. Two nonlinear models will be applied to the present case.

iii. It is possible that more than one independent variable is required for the model. The variation in the activity and variables may contain more than one piece of independent information. One variable selected for the model does not contain all the necessary information. One two-variable model will be applied to the present case.

B. Simple Nonlinear Models

The second alternative treatment of the data set is the use of nonlinear models. Two will be explored here. It has often been suggested that a quadratic (second order, parabolic) relationship is appropriate for data in drug studies. For the present case, eqn. 12 shows such a model written in the multiple linear form, however, rather than in an explicit quadratic form:

$$pC = b_0 + b_1 x_1 + b_2 x_2 \tag{12}$$

where $x_2 = (^1x^v)^2$.

The following statistics are obtained:

$$pC = -3.201 + 2.311 \, ^1x^v - 0.214(^1x^v)^2 \tag{13}$$
$$r = 0.936, \ s = 0.264, \ F = 38.8, \ n = 14$$

There is some general improvement in these statistics as compared to eqn. (7). However, it is always true that the addition of a variable will tend to improve the goodness of fit measures. Even a variable composed of random numbers will bring about some improvement. The important question is whether the improvement is statistically significant.

The question of statistical significance can be handled using the sequential and partial F tests mentioned above. The sequential F test shows the addition of the squared term not to be significant with a probability greater than 85% [100 (1. - .1484)]. The usual confidence level is taken to be 95%. Likewise, the partial F test shows that the squared term does not contribute significantly to reduction in sum squared error (P< 0.1484 or greater than 85%). This is especially noticeable when compared to the statistic for the linear term in $^1X^V$ which has a probability of 97%.

In addition, an examination of the residuals for this regression shows that no. 7 is still an outlier (res = -0.57), and the residuals are still not well distributed. On a statistical basis, the quadratic model can probably be rejected in this case. The addition of significantly more and well chosen data could raise the confidence if similar statistics resulted.

Another possible nonlinear model in this case is a hyperbolic equation; that is, inverse x as the independent variable. In fact, such a relation seems a possibility upon visual inspection of Figure 1. This model could be written in the simple linear form as follows:

$$y = b_0 + b_1 x_1 \qquad (14)$$

where $x_1 = 1/ \, ^1X^V$. It should be noted that this is the simplest form of a hyperbolic relation; in more complicated forms the variables may be written as $1/(x - a)$ and $1/(y - a')$, where a and a' are either known constants or constants to be determined. In the latter case, nonlinear least squares techniques are required (Wood and Daniel, 1980).

Regression analysis was performed on eqn. (14), and the results are shown in eqn. (15):

$$pC = -8.695x_1 + 4.741 \qquad (15)$$
$$r = 0.933, \; s = 0.258, \; F = 81.0, \; n = 14$$

or

$$pC = -8.695/^1X^V + 4.741$$

These statistics are also a slight improvement over eqn. (7). Observation no. 7 is still an outlier (res = -0.56); also the residual for phenol has increased significantly to 0.40. Statistically, there is little basis for selecting the hyperbolic model (regressed linearly) over the linear model. There is only a 7% decrease in standard error and the problem of residual distribution still remains.

If there were no further choices for models, one would be left with three models of very similar statistical significance. On the basis of simplicity, one might choose the simple linear model. The acquisition of well choosen additional data might provide better statistical grounds for choice. (For a discussion of potential problems in the use of linear regression on a nonlinear model, see Bevington (1969)).

4. Multivariate Linear Models

An examination of the residuals for the simple linear model, Table 1 and Figure 1, suggests one more model. The three largest negative residuals have a common feature in their molecular structure. They are the only compounds to have a substituent with strong hydrogen bonding capability. The three groups, $-OH$, $-NH_2$, $-COOH$, all can donate a highly positive hydrogen atom in a hydrogen bond. It may be that these values are atypical because they can participate in hydrogen bonding (at a position other than the phenolic OH), whereas the remaining 11 molecules cannot.

An alternative model could include a descriptor for hydrogen bonding capability:

$$pC = b_0 + b_1 x_1 + b_2 x_2 \qquad (16)$$

where $x_1 = {}^1x^v$ and $x_2 = HBOND$, the hydrogen bond descriptor. For purposes of this discussion, an indicator variable will be used; that is, the variable x_2 will be a two level variable: $x_2 = 1$ for the hydrogen bonding compounds 3, 7 and 9, whereas $x_2 = 0$ for the rest. (If the hydrogen bonding hypothesis appears reasonable or useful, one might pursue the question by developing a physical descriptor for use in place of the indicator variable.) Indicator variables are discussed by Wood and Daniel (1980).

TABLE 4.   Regression results on the conversion of cytochrome P-450
to P-420 using the first order valence chi index and a
hydrogen bond indicator variable.

GENERAL LINEAR MODELS PROCEDURE

Source	DF	Sum of Squares	Mean Square	F Value	Prob > F
Model	2	5.9811	2.9906	165.67	0.0001
Error	11	0.1986	0.0181		
Total	13	6.0807			

R Squared	0.9679
Correlation Coefficient	0.9838
Standard Deviation	0.1344

SOURCE (Type I)	DF	Sum of Squares	F Value	Prob > F
$^1\chi^v$	1	5.2525	290.98	0.0001
HBOND	1	0.7285	40.36	0.0001
(Type III)				
$^1\chi^v$	1	2.8900	160.10	0.0001
HBOND	1	0.7285	40.36	0.0001

Parameter	Estimate	t for H0: Parameter = 0	Prob > T
INTERCEPT	-0.3929	-2.07	0.0626
$^1\chi^v$	0.7436	12.65	0.0001
HBOND	-0.6161	-6.35	0.0001

TABLE 4. con't.

OBS	Activity	Calculated Activity	Lower 95% Predict	Upper 95% Predict	Residual
1	1.07	1.194	0.858	1.530	-0.124
2	2.09	2.076	1.765	2.384	0.014
3	1.60	1.556	1.237	1.870	0.046
4	0.81	0.675	0.335	1.020	0.132
5	1.50	1.499	1.180	1.818	0.000
6	1.82	1.916	1.607	2.225	-0.096
7	0.46	0.726	0.384	1.068	-0.266
8	1.48	1.499	1.180	1.818	-0.019
9	1.15	1.015	0.672	1.359	0.134
10	2.04	1.858	1.548	2.167	0.181
11	2.11	1.974	1.665	2.283	0.135
12	2.21	2.268	1.954	2.582	-0.058
13	2.65	2.632	2.302	2.963	0.017
14	2.90	2.996	2.638	3.355	-0.096

A statistical treatment of eqn. (16) yields the results in Table 4 and eqn. (17):

$$pC = 0.744 \, ^1\chi^v - 0.616 \, \text{HBond} - 0.333 \qquad (17)$$
$$r = 0.984, \quad s = 0.134, \quad F = 166, \quad n = 14$$

The statistics for this model are significantly improved over all the other models examined. The correlation coefficient and standard deviation are certainly better. A decrease of 50% in standard error is most significant. This means that the confidence interval on

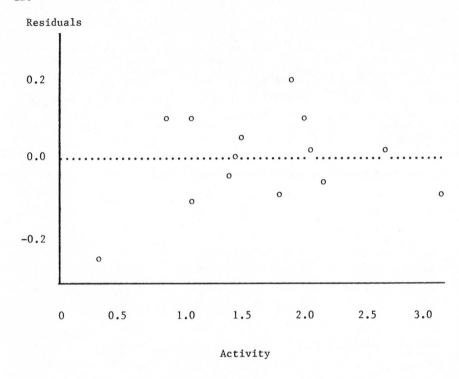

Residuals

FIGURE 3.   A plot of residuals against the observed activity in
the cytochrome P-450 regression using both the first
order valence chi index and the hydrogen bond indicator
variable.

predicted y values is about half as large. Further, both the
sequential F and partial F tests indicate high significance for the
coefficients. An examination of the residuals also shows considerable
improvement both in their magnitude (Table 4) and distribution
(Figure 3). From the purely statistical point of view, the two
variable model based on eqn. (16) is an excellent model. One note

of caution should be sounded here: the ratio of observations to variables is 7:1 for this case. This would seem to be a bit low, although general rules of thumb for the minimum value of this ratio run from 5 to 10. One must be very careful to have sufficient degrees of freedom to minimize the role of chance correlations. Some aspects of this question will be addressed later.

Note also that the second variable was not simply selected to apply to large residuals. It was selected on a common structural basis, namely, the possibility of hydrogen bonding.

5. Selection of a Model

Four models have been considered thus far. All four may be considered statistically significant and could be accepted on the basis of general QSAR experience. Which one should be used? This question should not be answered on purely statistical grounds. One may seek some theoretical basis of approach. Is hydrogen bonding expected to be important? Is activity expected to increase linearly without limit? Could there be an activity maximum or asymptotic limit? In any event, increasing the data set in order to test some of these questions (hypotheses) is one of the most profitable avenues of continued exploration. These models can serve as guidelines in the selection of additional compounds for testing and a basis of discrimination among models.

It should be remembered that the excellent goodness of fit for this model, including the good F tests for the hydrogen bonding variable, does not prove that hydrogen bonding is involved in this biological system. These results suggest that compounds 3, 7 and 9 may be unlike the rest of the data set. But unlike in what way? The indicator ascribes a constant contribution to the three compounds; perhaps, a variable contribution is more appropriate. The door is now open, however, to further exploration.

6. Selection of Few Variables from Many

If the model under consideration calls for specified variables, then these variables are entered into the regression program directly. Statistical results are evaluated and there is no question of which variables to use.

The more common situation in QSAR is that there are several variables which may be considered. The investigator must decide on the type of model as well as the number and identity of variables to be entered into the analysis. There are two types of questions to be answered once the type of model has been selected. (The general linear model will be considered here.) The two questions are the number of variables and the possibility of chance correlations.

Let us consider a specific example for this discussion. Hall and Kier (1984) have reported on the aquatic toxicity of a set of 25 phenols. The compounds and activities are shown in Table 5. The measure of activity is the molar concentration estimated to kill 50% of the fish, Pimephales promelas, in a standard flow-through test system. The dependent variable is the negative log of the molar concentration, LC_{50}:

$$pC = -\log(LC_{50})$$

For a data set containing 25 observations, it is reasonable to use two or three independent variables in the model and still retain sufficient degrees of freedom. In this discussion, statistical criteria will be considered in the determination of an appropriate number of variables but statistics will not be used alone.

In this present case many connectivity variables can be generated for the set of molecular structures. For this example, the following indexes were included in the data set: ^{0}X, ^{1}X, ^{2}X, $^{3}X_{p}$ through $^{6}X_{p}$, $^{3}X_{c}$, $^{4}X_{pc}$ and $^{6}X_{ch}$, in addition to the corresponding valence indexes. Some preliminary considerations could have trimmed the set somewhat. Experience suggests that the $^{6}X_{ch}$ and long path indexes

TABLE 5. Data for the acquatic toxicity of substituted
phenols against the fathead minnow.

Obs	Compound Name	Act [a]	^1X	$^3X^v_p$	Calc [b]	Res
1	Phenol	3.51	3.394	0.756	3.17	0.34
2	2-Chloro	4.02	3.805	1.172	3.63	0.39
3	2-Allyl	3.93	4.843	1.356	4.01	-0.08
4	4-Nitro	3.36	4.698	1.061	3.71	-0.35
5	3-Methoxy	3.21	4.326	1.053	3.63	-0.42
6	4-Butyl	4.47	5.326	1.755	4.47	0.00
7	4-tert-Butyl	4.46	4.999	1.733	4.38	0.08
8	4-Pentyl	5.18	5.826	2.005	4.80	0.38
9	4-tert-Pentyl	4.82	5.560	2.533	5.22	-0.40
10	2-Phenyl	4.45	6.377	1.989	4.87	-0.44
11	4-Phenylazo	5.26	7.343	1.887	5.00	0.26
12	4-Nonyl	6.20	7.826	3.005	6.11	0.09
13	2,4-Dichloro	4.30	4.198	1.448	3.96	0.34
14	4-Chloro-3-methyl	4.27	4.198	1.566	4.06	0.21
15	2,4-Dimethyl	3.86	4.198	1.352	3.87	-0.01
16	2,6-Dimethyl	3.74	4.215	1.439	3.95	-0.21
17	3,4-Xylenol	3.94	4.198	1.490	4.00	-0.06
18	4-Amino-2-nitro	3.65	5.109	1.196	3.92	-0.27
19	2,4-Dinitro	4.04	6.020	1.367	4.26	-0.22
20	2,4,6-Trichloro	4.33	4.609	1.776	4.34	-0.01
21	2,4,6-Tribromo	4.70	4.609	2.648	5.13	-0.43
22	2,4-Dinitro-o-cresol	4.99	6.430	1.673	4.62	0.37
23	2,3,4,5-Tetrachloro	5.72	5.037	2.825	5.38	0.34
24	Pentachloro	6.06	5.464	3.443	6.03	0.03
25	1-Naphthol	4.53	5.377	1.767	4.49	0.04

a) Hall, L. H., Kier, L. B., and Phipps, G. (1984).

b) Calculated from eqn. (19).

such as ^6X_p may not be important here. That would decrease the number of variables to 16; however, we retained 20 for the present study. (See Chapter 6 for a discussion of this question.)

How are the variables selected which will produce the best model? There are several avenues of approach to this question. If all the independent variables are truly independent, exactly orthogonal, then a stepwise procedure works well. The first variable selected is the one which accounts for the greatest variance. The next variable selected reduces the unexplained variance more than any other variable. The process continues until no further significant reduction in variance occurs. Stepwise methods are available in most widely used statistical packages.

The more common situation in QSAR is one in which the variables are not truly independent. If there are several variables, it may not be possible (reasonable experimentally) to select a data set in which all (independent) variables are simultaneously orthogonal. This is the usual case with connectivity indexes. A preliminary examination of the correlation matrix will reveal the situation. Because of the need to keep the number of variables at a reasonable minimum, one should not include: 1) variables which highly correlate with several other variables; and 2) variables with low or zero variance.

In the first case, it is usually possible to leave out one of a set of variables which highly intercorrelate. For example, the number of skeletal atoms usually correlates with ^0X, especially if the data set contains molecules of fairly homogeneous structure; that is, all noncyclic or all possessing one six-membered ring. In this case, the number of atoms is left out since ^0X does carry more information. Also, ^0X and ^1X may highly correlate for homogeneous data sets; ^0X is usually left out in such cases for the same reason.

In the second case, one does not include variables of low variance since they contribute little or nothing to the explanation of sample variance. For a data set with a very few cyclic compounds, $^6X_{ch}$ is usually left out. Likewise, if there are only a few molecules with 4-way branch points in the skeleton, ^4X_c may be left out. Of course, if these "unique" compounds are poorly explained, it may well be that their structural uniqueness needs to be described by a variable which was left out. In such cases, one should seek additional examples for the data set.

When the stepwise procedure seems inappropriate, then calculation of all possible regressions is the method choice. When considering a model with a small number of variables, 1-5, these methods are not overly time-consuming with current programs and computers. For the present example, the output is shown in Table 6. Options were selected which gave the best five regressions, judged on r^2, for one, two, and three-variable models. The best one and two-variable equations are shown here.

$$pC = 1.079^3X_p^v + 2.527 \qquad (18)$$
$$r = 0.903, \; s = 0.347, \; F = 101.5, \; n = 25$$

$$pC = 0.205^1X + 0.907^3X_p^v + 1.786 \qquad (19)$$
$$r = 0.934, \; s = 0.296, \; F = 74.6, \; n = 25$$

Statistics for eqn. (19) are also summarized in Table 7. The calculated activities and residuals based on eqn. (19) are shown in Table 5.

On simple statistical grounds, eqn. (18) is considered significant at a fairly high level; however, the best two variable equation, eqn. (19), is considerably better. The addition of the second variable ^1X is judged to be statistically significant as can be seen from Table 7. The sequential F-test based on Type I Sum of Squares is significant at the 99.48% level. The decrease in standard error is about 15%.

Is a third variable warranted? On a simple statistical basis the best three-variable model in Table 6 is judged to be significant. Each variable is also considered significant on the basis of both the sequential and partial F tests at a very high level, $P > 99.9\%$. On a more practical basis the addition of the third variable does not decrease the standard error very much; in fact, s decreases by less

TABLE 6.   Best regressions for one, two and three variables
for the   aquatic toxicity of substituted phenols.

N	R Squared	Standard Deviation	Variables in Model		
1	0.6730	0.462	$^2\chi^v$		
1	0.7289	0.421	$^5\chi_p^v$		
1	0.7432	0.409	$^1\chi^v$		
1	0.7780	0.381	$^0\chi^v$		
1	0.8153	0.347	$^3\chi_p^v$		
2	0.8531	0.316	$^3\chi_p^v$	$^4\chi_p^v$	
2	0.8561	0.313	$^3\chi_p$	$^5\chi_p^v$	
2	0.8592	0.310	$^3\chi_p^v$	$^5\chi_p$	
2	0.8623	0.307	$^3\chi_p^v$	$^0\chi$	
2	0.8714	0.296	$^3\chi_p^v$	$^1\chi$	
3	0.8801	0.293	$^3\chi_p^v$	$^1\chi^v$	$^1\chi_p^v$
3	0.8810	0.292	$^3\chi_p^v$	$^1\chi$	$^4\chi_p^v$
3	0.8826	0.290	$^3\chi_p^v$	$^5\chi_p$	$^4\chi_p$
3	0.8860	0.285	$^5\chi_p^v$	$^1\chi^v$	$^6\chi_p^v$
3	0.8939	0.275	$^5\chi_p^v$	$^3\chi_p$	$^4\chi_p$

TABLE 7. Regression analysis for aquatic toxicity of substituted phenols using the first order and the third order valence path chi indexes.

GENERAL LINEAR MODELS PROCEDURE

Source	DF	Sum of Squares	Mean Square	F Value	Prob > F
Model	2	13.0768	6.5384	74.55	0.0001
Error	22	1.9294	0.0877		
Total	24	15.0062			

R Squared		0.8714
Correlation Coefficient		0.9335
Standard Deviation		0.296

Source	DF	Type I Sum of Squares	F Value	Prob > F
$^{3}\chi^{v}$	1	12.2347	139.51	0.0001
$^{1}\chi$	1	0.8421	9.60	0.0052

Source	DF	Type III Sum of Squares	F Value	Prob > F
$^{3}\chi^{v}$	1	6.2840	71.65	0.0001
$^{1}\chi$	1	0.8421	9.60	0.0052

PARAMETER ESTIMATES

Variable	Estimate	t for HO: Parameter = 0	Prob > T
INTERCEPT	1.7864	6.06	0.0001
$^{3}\chi^{v}$	0.9067	8.46	0.0001
$^{1}\chi$	0.2045	3.10	0.0053

than 8%. Since the confidence interval on a predicted activity is directly proportional to s, very little is gained by adding the third variable.

The addition of the third variable, however, increases the possibility of chance correlations becoming significant in the regression model. By adding a third variable, the ratio of observations to variables decreases from 12.5 to 8.3. Perhaps, a better approach is to use eqn. (19) as a basis for selecting a few more compounds for testing. In this case there is a scarcity of data at high activity. If a few well chosen compounds are added to the data set, the degrees of freedom would be increased and the three variable model could be examined with more confidence. Certainly the choice of two variables is a conservative approach. If one plans to obtain more data, then the selection of compounds could well be guided by both eqn. (19) and the best three variable equation. If one is interested in good predictions rather than refinement of the model, then the two-variable equation is probably better.

Further considerations on the choice of variables and type of model will be discussed in the next chapter. So far it has been suggested that statistical considerations are a very important guide up to a point. Ultimately, practical experimental considerations must be brought to bear on the question. In this instance, the small improvement in standard error was used as a basis for decision.

An estimate of experimental error was based on replicate analyses. A standard deviation of ±0.15 log units was found (Hall, Kier and Phipps 1984). Eqn. (19) gives a standard deviation about twice that error. Perhaps, one should not look for a decrease in regression standard error but rather for good predicted values on new data or a stable model when new data is introduced into the regression data set. In fact, the two variable equation gives very good calculated activity values with no residual being greater than twice the regression standard error.

7. Chance Correlation - An Avenue of Exploration

In this case there is an increased possibility that regression statistics are affected by chance or random effects. When a regression equation is developed by selecting a few variables from a larger set, primarily on statistical grounds, the estimation of statistical significance based on the regression model alone appears to underestimate the probability of chance correlation. The confidence intervals on the regression coefficients are too small, reflected in smaller standard error and larger t values than may be warranted.

A. Use of Random Numbers

Topliss and Costello (1972) have pointed out these problems and warned that QSAR investigators must be careful in their application of statistical techniques. Kier and Hall (1977) have suggested a direct approach to the problem which will be applied to the present example and was reported recently (Hall and Kier, 1984). Two statistical approaches will be used here.

The question of chance correlations is often answered in terms of the variance ratio or F test; however, this test is based on an assumption of exactly normal distributions and exactly orthogonal or independent variables, and does not in any way take into account the effect of the selection of few variables from a larger data set. A direct and perhaps brute force approach to this question may be best for a given data set. In this approach the larger data set is replaced by random numbers. For the phenol toxicity set, each chi index is replaced by random numbers, that is, 20 vectors of 25 random numbers each. The whole data matrix except for the activity is replaced by random numbers and then the same statistical program is used to compute the best regression statistics.

Since we are interested in the nature of eqn. (19), we examined all possible two-variable regressions and stored the correlation statistics for the best equation. This procedure was repeated 100 times and all the r values along with the best correlation coefficient for both one and two variables equations was stored for analysis. A histogram of these values is printed and examined. This data is given in Table 8. (All these features were incorporated into a FORTRAN program RANDR.) For the one-variable model, the highest r is r = 0.596 and for the two-variable model it is r = 0.717. It is easy to see that these correlation coefficients are significantly worse than those reported for chi variables in eqns. (18) and (19). The models based on one and two variable linear equations using chi indexes are significantly different from those based on random numbers.

For the two variable random number model, a total of 19,000 two-variable regressions were computed -- all possible two variable combinations in a 20 variable data set repeated 100 times. This is equivalent to the combinations of r objects in a set of n objects, P(n,r), and removing the r! permutations of equivalent arrangements:

$$N = P(n,r)/r! = n!/r!(n - r)!$$

In the 19,000 regressions computed for the two-variable case, only two were found with r > 0.70; the largest is r = 0.717. It may be concluded in this case that the chance of a random correlation having r > 0.70 is approximately 2 in 19,000 or about 0.011%. The probability for r > 0.90 is considerably smaller but not known for the calculations made in the 100 runs.

These results indicate that the two-variable model, selected from the 20 variable set to obtain eqn. (19), is statistically significant. Note, however, that the probability estimated in this fashion is more than the probability calculated from the standard F test, much less than 0.011%, for eqn. (19). This difference reflects the fact that the direct method illustrated here takes into account the selection of the few-from-many process.

Another approach is to keep the independent variables in the regression equation while replacing the activity with random numbers. For the present case the random number "activity" vector

TABLE 8. Correlation coefficients computed from random number variables for a two-variable model for phenol aquatic toxicity data.

All Correlations

Range of r	.0-.1	.1-.2	.2-.3	.3-.4	.4-.5	.5-.6	.6-.7	.7-.8	.8-.9	.9-1.
Number of Values	2039	4945	5545	3897	1835	647	90	2	0	0
Percentage	10.7	26.0	29.2	20.5	9.7	3.4	.5	.01	0	0

Correlation for "Best" Regression in Each Run
100 Runs

Range of r	.0-.1	.1-.2	.2-.3	.3-.4	.4-.5	.5-.6	.6-.7	.7-.8	.8-.9	.9-1.
Number of Values	0	0	0	2	21	50	25	2	0	0

is regressed against the matrix containing the ^1X and $^3X_p^v$ index values. In this manner, the "peculiarities" of the independent variables (such as range of values and intercorrelations) are preserved.

For this phenol toxicity data set, 1,000 runs were made using different sets of random numbers for the activity. Two values were found with $r > 0.7$, the largest being 0.708. The average r is 0.254. These values are significantly less than found in the regression of the true activity against ^1X and $^3X_p^v$. On the basis of

138

this information, the probability that a random correlation will produce $r > 0.70$ is about 2 in 1000 or $P < 0.02$: The probability that $r > 0.90$ would occur is considerably less than 0.02%.

Using this approach, it is possible to examine directly the possibility that random effects produce a regression of similar quality to the QSAR model. In successive treatments first the independent variables and then the activity is replaced with random numbers. The probability that the QSAR model is not different from a random correlation computed as above is always larger than that given by standard regression methods. These estimated probabilities are likely more realistic. Another example of this treatment is given in Chapter 7.

B. Statistical Stability of the Regression Model

In a second approach to the statistical significance question, the stability of the final equation is examined. The actual statistics including regression coefficients depend upon the specific data included in the data set; that is, the molecules in the data set and the range of activity values define the space in which the regression is carried out. The extent of this space with respect to each variable and the density of points throughout the space have a direct influence on the details of the computed statistical quantities.

Some sense of the relation between computed statistics and variation in data set should be acquired as part of the QSAR analysis. In many respects, this may be simulated by leaving out part of the data and then repeating the regression calculation. This process may be repeated, leaving out a different group of observations, and then repeating over and over until all observations have been left out at least once. This approach is related to what is sometimes called the jackknife method. (Gray and Shucany, 1972)

The stability of the regression model may be evaluated by the variation in computed statistics. If random correlations were playing an important role in the regression model, it would be expected that the model would not be highly stable with respect to random deletions of a small subset of the data.

An immediate question arises: how many variables to delete? This question can be subdivided into two parts: (1) How many observations should be left out for a given calculation (run); and (2) how many runs should be made for a given number of deletions. The strategy adopted here is as follows. Use a random process to delete n observations and run the regression program. Then, delete another n randomly selected observations and rerun the regression program. Repeat the process until all of the observations have been deleted at least once. In this manner, the influence of each observation plays a role in the final computations. (This approach was implemented in a FORTRAN program JACKN).

For the present case, several possibilities were examined. The number of observations deleted was varied (2, 3, 4, 6, 8, 10, 12, 15), and the number runs (5, 10, 15, 20, 25, 30, 40, 50), also. Two effects were found: a) as the number of observations deleted was increased, the model eventually became unstable; and b) for a given number of deleted observations, the stability of the model leveled off as the number of runs increased. Perhaps, these results are not unexpected, and only a brief commentary is needed.

The effect of varying number of observations deleted is indicated at the bottom of Table 9. The number deleted was varied from 2 to 15, or from 8% to 60% of the data set. Ten runs were made for each number deleted using random selection of the deleted observations on each run. The only restriction placed on the random selection is that in the 10 runs no observation could be deleted more than a preselected limit. As the number deleted increases, the limit must also increase. For 2 and 4 deletions, their limit was set at 4; but for 6 deletions, the limit was 10.

As can be seen from the bottom of Table 9, the model is quite stable for 2 deletions; similar results were obtained for 3 and 4 deletions. However, as the number deleted becomes a larger fraction of the data set, instability eventually appears as indicated by the range in regression values given. It is, of course, not surprising

TABLE 9.   Information for test of statistical stability of regression
model for aquatic toxicity of substituted phenols.

	Original Model (no deletions)		3 Deletions per Run (30 runs)	
	Regression Value	Standard Deviation	Average Value	Standard Deviation
Correlation Coefficient	0.934		0.933	0.010
Standard Deviation	0.296	0.004	0.297	0.011
Coefficient of ^1X: b_1	0.205	0.004	0.204	0.026
Coefficient of $^3X_p^v$: b_2	0.906	0.011	0.906	0.038
Constant: b_0	1.786	0.295	1.787	0.107
Average Residual	0.231		0.254	0.171
Residuals less than one standard deviation	56.0%		51.1%	
Residuals between one and two standard deviations	44.0%		48.9%	
Residuals greater than two standard deviations	0.0%		0.0%	

VARIATION IN STATISTICS WITH NUMBER OF OBS. DELETED

No. of Obs. Del.	r Ave.	Range in r	b_2 Ave.	Range in b_2	b_1 Ave.	Range in b_1	b_0 Ave.	Range in b_0
0	.934	–	.906	–	.205	–	1.79	–
2	.934	.92-.94	.914	.88-.97	.208	.17-.24	1.75	1.53-1.92
6	.932	.91-.94	.913	.83-.98	.186	.16-.24	1.86	1.72-2.07
10	.933	.89-.97	.947	.78-1.03	.193	.11-.29	1.78	1.14-2.18

Regression Equation: $pC = b_0 + b_1 {}^1X + b_2 {}^3X_p^v$

that there should be variation in the regression model as larger data subsets are removed from the set. The degrees of freedom are significantly diminished. Further, it may well be that the observations are not uniformly related to each variable; that is, there is no requirement that each variable have the same relation to the data set. Consider a data set consisting of straight chain compounds and several simply branched isomers. Perhaps, the model may contain two indexes, ^1X and $^4X_{pc}$. The ^1X index has a non-zero value for all the molecules; each molecule, then, contributes directly to the coefficient of ^1X. On the other hand, only branched compounds have nonzero $^4X_{pc}$ indexes; thus, if most of the branched compounds are removed in a random subset deletion, the coefficient of $^4X_{pc}$ could be drastically affected. The same effect would be observed for parameters such as log P and Hammett sigma for a mixed set of nonpolar and highly polar substituents on a benzene ring.

As a result of this observation, it is recommended that no more than approximately 10% of the data set be deleted. The overall results of the deletion study are summarized at the top of Table 9. The left hand side shows the results of the standard regression as done for eqn. (19). The right hand side shows the results of deleting three observations (12%), selected on a random basis, 30 times. The tabulated results are the average and standard deviation for each quantity. The very favorable comparison of the two sides of the table indicates that the regression model is very stable with respect to choice of data set. This is clearly indicated by the low standard deviation for each of the statistical quantities shown. In this study, each observation was deleted at least once; no observation was deleted more than 4 times, and most observations were deleted 3 or 4 times.

Notice that the standard deviation on the regression coefficients from the deletion study are larger than those obtained from the straight regression analysis. It may be that the best estimate of standard error lies somewhere between the two but the larger number may be more realistic.

In this study when an observation was deleted (not included in a current regression calculation), a value was computed for the activity. This "predicted" value was compared to the observed and the difference (a kind of "residual") stored. An analysis of these "residuals" is given at the middle of Table 9. These values also compare favorably to those for the straight regression. This aspect of the study has important bearing on the predictive quality of the model.

In this present case, all the studies suggest that the model based on eqn. (19) is a sound statistical model. Both the random number analysis and the deletion procedure have been applied to several connectivity based models. In each case, the models have shown substantial statistical soundness.

8. Conclusion

Standard statistical methods are employed for QSAR analysis using molecular connectivity indexes. Simple linear as well a multiple linear models may be used. Simple nonlinear cases may also be handled in the multiple linear fashion.

Molecular connectivity indexes may be calculated for a variety of structure features. For this reason, many indexes may be generated for a given list of molecules. For molecules with a somewhat homogeneous set of structures the list of chi indexes may be trimmed down by a combination of structural intuition and statistical criteria. More will be said of this question in Chapter 6. For molecules with a wide variety of structure features the chi indexes afford great opportunity to find the best description of those structures and the mathematical relation to activity in the statistically determined QSAR model. Of course, the use of molecular connectivity is not limited to the types of analyses reviewed in this chapter. When statistical criteria are used as the primary basis for selection of a few variables from a larger set, questions of the statistical significance of the resulting model must be addressed. A method based on use of random numbers has shown in several cases that models based on chi indexes stand the test. Further, the connectivity models also appear to be stable with respect to selection of the data set. Now that these basic questions of statistical methodology have been addressed, further aspects of strategy can be explored. Several of these areas of interest are addressed in the next chapter.

References

Allen, D. M. and Cady, F. B. (1982). Analyzing Experimental Data by Regression, Belmont, CA: Lifetime Learning Publications.

Bard, J. (1974). Nonlinear Parameter Estimation, New York: Academic Press.

Bevington, P. R. (1969). Data Reduction and Error Analysis for the Physical Sciences, New York: McGraw-Hill Book Co.

Cattell, R. B. (1966). The Scientific Use of Factor Analysis, New York: Plenum Press.

Daniel, C. and Wood, F. (1980). Fitting Equations to Data (Revised Edition), New York: John Wiley and Sons.

Draper, N. and Smith, H. (1981). Applied Regression Analysis, Second Edition, New York: John Wiley and Sons.

Freund, R. J. and Littell, R. C. (1981). SAS for Linear Models, Cary, N.C.: SAS Institute.

Gorsuch, R. L. (1974). Factor Analysis, Philadelphia: W. B. Saunders Co.

Gray, H. L. and Shucany, W. R. (1972). The Generalized Jackknife Statistic, New York: Marcel-Dekker.

Hall, L. H. and Kier, L. B. (1984). Molecular connectivity of phenols and their toxicity to fish. Bull. Environ. Contam. Toxicol., 32, 354-362.

Hall, L. H., Kier, L. B. and Phipps, G., (1984). SAR studies on the toxicities of benzene derivatives I. An additivity model. Environ. Toxicol. Chem., 3, 255-262.

Ichikawa, Y. and Yamano, T. (1967). The role of hyrogen bonding in P-450 and the effect of organic compounds on the conversion to P-420. Biochim. Biophys. Acta. 147, 518-524.

Morrison, D. R. (1976). Multivariate Statistical Methods, Second Edition, New York: McGraw-Hill Book Co..

Mosteller, F. and Tukey, J. W. (1977). Data Analysis and Regression, Reading, MA. Addison-Wesley.

Neter, J. and Wasserman, W. (1974). Applied Linear Statistical Models, Homewood, IL: Irwin.

Overall, J. E. and Klett, C. J. (1972). Applied Multivariate Analysis, New York: McGraw-Hill.

Rao, C. R. (1973). Linear Statistical Inference and Its Applications, Second Edition, New York: John Wiley and Sons.

Topliss, J. and Costello, R. (1972). Chance factors in studies on quantitative structure-activity relationships. J. Med. Chem., 15, 1066-1072.

CHAPTER 6

Strategies for the Use of Molecular Connectivity

The molecular connectivity indexes provide the investigator with an array of quantitative descriptions of molecules, encoding information about molecular structure such as size, shape, branching, unsaturation and heteroatom content. The significance of some of the more commonly occurring indexes has been reviewed in two earlier chapters. Basic statistical considerations were discussed in the preceding chapter. The employment of these indexes in QSAR studies requires a number of considerations which will be discussed in this chapter. Consideration will be given to selection of connectivity indexes and choice of the form of mathematical model. Further, it is often useful to include in a study additional physical properties and structural parameters. In QSAR analysis, statistical methods other than regression are used and some will be discussed here.

1. Selection of Chi Indexes for Regression

The choice of chi indexes in the search for the best variables in a regression analysis is important. Chi indexes should not be included in a search when the numerical values are constant or zero for more than a few of the compounds. This criterion avoids the bias of chi indexes which are exclusive for a limited part of the compound list. A corollary to this rule is to select indexes in the analysis which have a nonzero value for most of the compounds in the list. The valence indexes are included for study when heteroatoms are varied in a list of compounds. The same rule holds true if unsaturation or aromatic rings are prominent in the compound list.

In the routine computation of chi indexes by computer program,* many indexes may be generated. In the usual case, about 22 indexes are computed and stored in a computer file for subsequent selection in an analysis. These indexes include ^0X, ^1X, ^2X, ^3X_p through ^6X_p, ^3X_c, $^4X_{pc}$, $^6X_{ch}$, and the corresponding valence indexes. In most studies only part of this list would actually be retained, depending upon the structure details of the list of molecules in the data set. For example, if the molecules are noncyclic, the chain terms would all be zero. Likewise, if there are no four-way branch points, the ^4X_c index is zero. Less obvious structural considerations will now be examined.

A. Alkyl Sidechains

A number of points are illustrated in Table 1. What chi indexes would be selected for a regression search? In List 1, the longest path in any of the compounds is 8 for the butyl derivative. Four other derivatives have a maximum of 7 path lengths. The remaining four have at least 6 path lengths. No path index with order higher than 6 should be considered for a search. There are 4 path lengths within the common urethane structure; hence, useful information about the nature of the R groups could be obtained by selecting no more than the first three path length indexes. These reflect structural variation occurring beyond the urethane group in the R side chain.

Only four of the nine compounds in List 1 are branched in the R moiety. Only these would have ^3X_c or $^4X_{pc}$ indexes different from the five normal alkyl urethanes. Accordingly, we may include ^3X_c and $^4X_{pc}$ in our search as well as the ^1X, ^2X, ^3X_p indexes. There

---

* Program CFUNC in FORTRAN may be obtained from L. H. Hall.

TABLE 1. Urethanes illustrating parameter selection.

$$R-NH-CO-O-CH_2-CH_2$$

R List 1	R List 2
CH_3	phenyl
CH_3CH_2	p-CH_3-phenyl
$CH_3CH_2CH_2$	p-CH_3O-phenyl
$(CH_3)_2CH$	p-NO_2-phenyl
$CH_3(CH_2)_3$	p-NH_2-phenyl
$CH_3CH_2CH(CH_3)$	o-CH_3-phenyl
$(CH_3)_3C$	o-Cl-phenyl
$(CH_3CH_2)_2CH$	o-NH_2-phenyl
$(CH_3)_3CCH_2$	p-Br-phenyl
	o-OCH_3-phenyl
	m-Cl-phenyl
	m-CH_3-phenyl
	m-NO_2-phenyl
	m-CH_3O-phenyl
	o-Br-phenyl

are no heteroatoms in the R groups; hence, valence connectivity indexes give no additional information. Finally, the ^0X index correlates significantly with ^1X for this data set and hence would be excluded.

For a study of the QSAR of molecules in List 1, we conclude that the indexes ^1X, ^2X, ^3X_p, ^3X_c, and $^4X_{pc}$ reveal an optimum amount of information about structure for an analysis. It might be prudent to include ^4X_p in the event that a change in the slope of activity versus chain length occurs with these molecules. Thus, five or six indexes would be computed and used in a regression analysis leading to a one-variable equation. A two-variable equation would not be as reliable, there being fewer observations than is desirable.

B. Heteroatom Substituents

List 2 in Table 1 presents a different set of circumstances. The maximum path length of the R groups is constant to within two path lengths. The principal variation is in the heteroatom substituent on a benzene ring. As a consequence, the low-order path indexes, $^1X^V$ and $^2X^V$, must be included to differentiate the heteroatoms in the list. The ^3X_c reflects the count of branches on the rings, one in every case but the first; thus, this index may not fully discriminate structural variation. In contrast, the $^4X^V_{pc}$ index is very useful in quantifying the presence, position, type and length of the ring substituent (Kier 1980a). The $^6X^V_{ch}$ index is nearly constant through the series, so it would not be included in a search.

In this particular case, principal component analysis may be used to assist in the selection of indexes. When the data set is subjected to principal component analysis, the set of variables is transformed into linear combinations of the variables called eigenvectors. Associated with each eigenvector is an eigenvalue which represents the fraction of variance in the data set which is related to that eigenvector. In other words the amount of information contained in each eigenvector is revealed by the principal component analysis. The usual rule of thumb is that the number of eigenvectors required to account for 95-98% of the data variance is equal to the number of independent variables or pieces of information actually in the data set.

In the urethane example principal component analysis of the whole set of 22 chi variables (listed earlier) indicates that 4 variables account for 94.8%, and 5 variables account for 98.0% of the variation. The percentages for the first 5 eigenvectors are 48.7, 34.4, 7.5, 4.2 and 3.2%. The reason that there are only five independent pieces of information is that there are correlations among certain of the chi indexes for this data set, arising from the structural interrelations in the molecules. Principal component analysis may be used to narrow down the set of variables which can be examined profitably. For this set, skeletal variety is very limited: only one type of ring possessed by all molecules, no 4-way branch points, only one substituent on the benzene ring. In this situation, ^0X and ^1X (as well as $^0X^V$ and $^1X^V$) carry very similar information; therefore, ^0X and $^0X^V$ are no longer considered. This is a very general pattern for structures similar to this data set; however, the two indexes ^1X and $^1X^V$ do not carry the same information. From a principal component analysis, the two eigenvectors carry 64% and 36% of the variance. This is essentially the same result as when ^0X, $^0X^V$, ^1X, $^1X^V$ are considered together, and so it is reasonable to retain only ^1X and $^1X^V$.

The contribution from other terms can now be considered. When the longer path terms, ^2X, ^3X_p, ^4X_p, ^5X_p, and ^6X_p, are added to ^1X, very little additional information is added. The first two principal components account for 90% and 6% of the variation, respectively. For this data set, one need not consider all of these path indexes. More information is added when the corresponding valence indexes are considered. Three eigenvectors account for 53.1%, 38.1%, and 4.0% of the variance. Some useful additional information is contained in the simple and valence path terms but not all of them are needed.

Examination of the ^3X_c and $^4X_{pc}$ indexes indicates that they contain significant information. The set of indexes ^1X, $^1X^V$, $^3X_c^V$, and $^4X_{pc}^V$ contains three significant eigenvectors: 65%, 29% and 5%. It seems clear that the path indexes contain some information as do the cluster and path/cluster indexes. Just what set of indexes is it useful to examine?

The minimum set which contains four significant eigenvectors consists of ^1X, $^1X^V$, ^3X_c, $^3X_c^V$, $^4X_{pc}$, and $^4X_{pc}^V$. One may wish to add path indexes such as ^6X_p and $^6X_p^V$ or ^2X and $^2X^V$. The long path indexes are sensitive to substitution pattern around a benzene ring as is the ^2X index. Further, the principal variation in this set of structures is heteroatom differences. For this reason, the valence indexes are much more important; so some of the simple indexes may be left out. A suggested set of indexes which maximizes information but minimizes the number of indexes examined is as follows: $^1\chi$, $^2\chi$, $^3\chi_c$, $^4\chi_{pc}$, $^1\chi^v$, $^2\chi^v$, $^5\chi_p^v$, $^6\chi_p^v$, $^3\chi_c^v$ and $^4\chi_{pc}^v$. These ten indexes form a statistically reasonable set from which to select the best set in a QSAR model.

Generally, it is possible to select a reasonable set of chi indexes for a given study. The less structure variation in the data set, the fewer the indexes that are needed. For some QSAR problems the set selected above will be quite adequate. If there is greater substitution variety, then other path indexes become important. Also, the $^6\chi_{ch}$ and $^7\chi_{ch}$ indexes reflect structure around rings and may be added when their variation is significant. It is usually possible to create a data set containing from 8 to 18 indexes. When careful and proper statistical analysis is performed, the larger set may be used. If in doubt about which ones to include in the typical QSAR study which involves several kinds of atoms in different sites in the molecule and includes some skeletal variety, the following set is recommended: $^1\chi$, $^2\chi$, $^3\chi_p$ to $^6\chi_p$, $^3\chi_c$, $^4\chi_{pc}$, $^6\chi_{ch}$, along with the corresponding valence indexes.

If the time and effort required to compute any index up to, say, a sixth-order index is not a factor, simply include all indexes up through the sixth order, relying on a computer to calculate the indexes and perform the regression analyses. Even under these circumstances, it is still necessary to eliminate indexes for cases in which they obviously play no role in structural differentiation.

2. Abbreviation of Molecular Structure

Returning to List 1 in Table 1, can we abbreviate these structures and calculate molecular connectivity indexes for just the R groups and retain the same information content? The answer is a qualified yes. The retention of information germane to the property under study depends upon the possible interrelation between parts of R substituents and the urethane moiety. If a branched carbon in R, three atoms removed from the carbonyl group, is essential, then the carbonyl group must be explicitly considered in the chi indexes to maximize the information content. Consideration of just the R groups may fail to provide the proper emphasis on this structural feature. A different set of chi indexes and coefficients might arise from a regression analysis, which may yield a correlation of a quality near that for a consideration of the whole molecule.

A test of this aspect of molecular connectivity analysis was made on a study of LSD analogs (Glennon and Kier, 1978) (see Table 2). The analysis of the LSD analogs using the complete molecule gave a satisfactory set of statistics. Abbreviation of the molecule to retain structural features within about five path lengths of the amide, structure II, yielded the same statistical quality as in the first equation. Severe truncation to a model containing only the variable features on the nitrogen, structure III, resulted in a decline in the quality of the correlation. We can abbreviate molecular structure in a series up to a point where all essential features necessary for activity are included. Further truncation results in loss of information and a probable decline in the statistical quality of the correlations.

It is not always easy to assess by inspection what may be important in a structure. In the LSD example in Table 2, our intuition might guide us to choose model II as a reasonable compromise in abbreviating the structures. This is true because we have extended the structure in the model to five path lengths beyond the variable amide group. Structure beyond that point is constant in the series. In contrast, model III should be suspect from the start since an important polar heteroatom, the carbonyl oxygen, has been deleted. Further, we do not go beyond the amide group more than one path length; thus, any interplay between amide and ring, as a necessary feature, is not studied using this model.

A general rule might be: truncate a large structure for molecular connectivity calculations to retain major structural features which may play a role in interacting with the variable part of the molecule.

TABLE 2. Correlation coefficients and structures for three different levels of molecule representation.

I	II	III
r = 0.940	r = 0.941	r = 0.924
s = 0.196	s = 0.195	s = 0.220

Model I: Log RBR = 24.94 - 0.835 ^2X - 0.917 ^6X_p - 1/0.0072 $^0X^v$

Retention of all features up to six path lengths beyond the varying part of a molecular series is likely to accomplish that objective.

One further comment on abbreviating structures deals with possible subsequent studies in which another part of the molecule is varied. If we were to use model II in Table 2 for an analysis of LSD QSAR, and then later on vary the structures in another position such as the indole ring, the truncated model could not be used. It would be necessary to repeat the first study using a new model which would permit structural variation on a second part of the molecule. It may be better to have used model I right from the start.

3. Substructure/Subgraph Analysis

Each chi index is a summation of terms, one for each subgraph of the specific type which occurs in the molecular skeleton. For ^1X, the subgraph type is simply the skeletal bond. For this reason, the number of contributors to ^1X tends to be fairly uniform; that is, evenly distributed throughout the structure.

Other indexes, however, are more heavily dependent on particular structural features. Some molecules give rise to an increased number of certain subgraph types. For example, there is only one ^2X subgraph associated with a methylene or ether linkage, a nonbranched skeletal point. For a three-way branch there are 3 paths of length two, and for a four-branch point there are six subgraphs of length two. On a benzene ring, a single non-hydrogen atom substituent (-Cl, -OH, $-CH_3$, etc.) contributes two $^4X_{pc}$ type subgraphs, while two substituents in an ortho relation contribute six subgraphs.

On this basis, features of molecular structure contribute to each index in varying ways. It could prove useful to examine the subgraph contributions to each of the terms in a regression equation. It may be possible to isolate structural features which are more important to an activity. These features could be helpful in understanding the mechanism of action.

Berger and colleagues (1953) studied the antimicrobial activity of 28 substituted phenylpropylethers tested against Tricophyton mentagrophytes. Hall and Kier (1978a) reported on the regression analysis of these compounds. The following equation and statistics were obtained:

$$pC = 2.44 \; ^1X - 3.29 \; ^3X_p + 2.71 \; ^4X_{pc}^v - 1.31 \qquad (1)$$
$$r = 0.957, \; s = 0.149, \; F = 87.4, \; n = 28$$

These results are summarized in Table 3.

An examination of the general structure of the molecule suggests two areas of interest. The hydroxy or dihydroxy substitution on the propyl group is certainly an area of potential specific interaction through hydrogen bonding. This area will be labelled the X/Y region. The other area of possible interest is the substitution pattern on the phenyl ring.

TABLE 3. Antimicrobial activity for substituted phenylpropylethers.
R-Ph-O-CH$_2$-CHX-CHY

No.	Substituent R	X	Y	^1X	^3X_p	$^4X_{pc}^v$	Act	Calc
1	2-Methyl	OH	OH	6.236	4.016	0.505	2.26	2.09
2	2-Methyl	OH	H	5.843	3.468	0.394	2.46	2.65
3	2-Methyl	H	OH	5.698	3.404	0.469	2.79	2.76
4	2-Chloro	OH	OH	6.236	4.016	0.543	2.31	2.21
5	2-Chloro	OH	H	5.843	3.468	0.432	2.84	2.77
6	4-Chloro	OH	OH	6.220	3.900	0.455	2.31	2.28
7	4-Chloro	OH	H	5.826	3.351	0.345	2.81	2.84
8	4-Chloro	H	OH	5.682	3.288	0.419	3.07	2.95
9	2,6-Dichloro	OH	OH	6.647	4.470	0.807	2.37	2.49
10	2,6-Dichloro	OH	H	6.253	3.922	0.697	3.04	3.04
11	2,4-Dichloro	OH	H	6.236	3.788	0.623	3.35	3.22
12	2,4-Dichloro	OH	OH	6.630	4.336	0.734	2.61	2.66
13	2-Methyl-4-chloro	OH	H	6.236	3.788	0.587	3.30	3.10
14	2-Methyl-4-chloro	OH	OH	6.630	4.336	0.697	2.33	2.55
15	3-Methyl-4-chloro	OH	OH	6.630	4.471	0.904	2.90	2.74
16	3-Methyl-4-chloro	OH	H	6.236	3.923	0.793	3.30	3.30
17	2-Methyl-6-chloro	OH	OH	6.647	4.470	0.772	2.33	2.37
18	2-Methyl-6-chloro	OH	H	6.253	3.922	0.661	2.70	2.93
19	2-Methyl-6-chloro	H	OH	6.109	3.858	0.736	2.78	3.04
20	2,6-Dimethyl-4-chloro	OH	OH	7.041	4.700	0.915	2.76	2.97
21	2,6-Dimethyl-4-chloro	OH	H	6.647	4.151	0.804	3.51	3.53
22	2,6-Dimethyl-4-chloro	H	OH	6.503	4.087	0.879	3.51	3.64
23	3,5-Dimethyl-4-chloro	OH	OH	7.041	4.970	1.254	3.24	3.13
24	2,4,6-Trimethyl	OH	OH	7.041	4.700	0.881	3.10	2.87
25	3,5-Dimethyl-4-chloro	OH	H	6.647	4.421	1.143	3.68	3.69
26	2,4,6-Trimethyl	OH	H	6.647	4.151	0.770	3.46	3.42
27	3,5-Dimethyl-4-chloro	H	OH	6.503	4.358	1.247	3.93	3.89
28	2,6-Dimethyl-4-chloro	H	OH	6.503	4.087	0.867	3.67	3.60

Examination of the list of compounds in Table 3 shows that the two most active molecules, nos. 25 and 27, have the largest $^4X_{pc}^v$ indexes. These have the 3,4,5 substitution pattern on the phenyl ring. It may be important to represent this region in the subgraph analysis. The negative coefficient of the ^3X_p index in eqn. 1 suggests an unfavorable contribution from this fragment. It is also clear that the 1,2-dihydroxy moiety in the X/Y region is unfavorable for high activity. Since there is one additional path-three type subgraph for the 1,2-dihydroxy pattern (as opposed to either the 1- or 2- pattern), it may be that the ^3X_p index is most informative for the X/Y region. Further, both the ^3X_p and $^4X_{pc}^v$ indexes are higher for the 3,4,5 pattern of substitution on the phenyl ring. The ^3X_p index, however, is unaffected by the presence of hetero-atoms, whereas the valence index $^4X_{pc}^v$ is increased by the presence of chlorine. For this present study, it may be useful to explore the role of the ^3X_p subgraphs associated with the X/Y region and the $^4X_{pc}^v$ subgraphs associated with the para region of the phenyl ring.

Since each index is a summation of subgraph terms, it is possible to factor out those terms associated with a particular structural feature or region. This may be done by hand more easily than by computer. For the phenylpropylethers, we consider the X/Y region in association with the ^3X_p index and the ring para region for the $^4X_{pc}^v$ index. The symbol $^m\bar{S}_t$ is used to denote the subgraph term(s) associated with the particular (restricted) aspect of structure being considered. Thus, $^3\bar{S}_p$ stands for the subgraph terms of interest in the simple path-three type index, ^3X_p.

In this case, $^3\bar{S}_p$ is the sum of all path-three subgraphs which include the OH at position X, or position Y or both. These subgraphs include molecular fragments such as $-OCH_2CHOH$, $-CH_2CHCH_2OH$, $-CH(OH)CH_2OH$, and $-CH_2CH_2CH_2OH$. The $^4\bar{S}_{pc}^v$ symbol stands for only those valence path/cluster-four subgraphs which contain a para substituent on the phenyl ring. Some examples of these subgraphs include $-CH-C(CH_3)-CHCH-$, $-CH-CClCHCH-$, $-CC(CH_3)CC-$, $-C(CH_3)-C(Cl)CH-$, etc., in which the para position carbon atom is always included as a three-way branch point. Each of the specified subgroups is identified and the corresponding contribution computed by the usual reciprocal square root equation.

For this case, a simple approach is used to determine whether these limited portions of the chi indexes carry a large portion of the significant structure information. The indexes in the regression equation, eqn. 1, are replaced by the corresponding subgraph index: $^3\bar{S}_p$ replaces ^3X_p, $^4\bar{S}^v_{pc}$ replaces $^4X^v_{pc}$, and the ^1X index is retained in its entirety since each of the structural features considered contribute no additional subgraphs to the ^1X index. If the subgraph terms do not carry the important information about the structure-activity relation, then the regression statistics will not compare favorably with those of eqn. (1).

If the correlation coefficient for the equation with the subgraph terms is not greatly diminished, it can be concluded that these subgraph terms carry much of the information which is important for this set of structures and activities. This, in fact, is the actual observation. The regression with ^1X, $^3\bar{S}_p$ and $^4\bar{S}^v_{pc}$ gives a correlation coefficient of $r = 0.924$. Other combinations of subgraph terms may be considered in order to refine this information; however, this analysis suggests strongly that the X/Y region and the para region are important to activity in this data set.

Another example of subgraph analysis is presented in Chapter 7 where the molecules are substituted benzimidazoles. A detailed dissection of the structure is possible in that case.

4. Non-Linear Equations

Molecular connectivity indexes have been employed in QSAR equations in non-linear form. Quadratic expressions have described relationships between a connectivity index and a property or more commonly, a biological activity.

$$\text{Activity} = ax + bx^2 + c$$

An equation of this form is derived from a property or structural descriptor and a quantitative value of a biological activity. An inspection of the data from a preliminary plotting of some representative part of the data may reveal a non-linear relationship.

A danger arises when a quadratic equation is found to be well correlated with data which does not reflect the whole region of the parabola. (This is revealed as a small coefficient of the squared term.) The presumption of a parabolic model from such an equation leads to predictions of a maximum and a region of declining potency beyond the maximum value of a structural descriptor. A case in point is a study of the antimicrobial effects of a series of halogenated phenols (Hall and Kier, 1978b).

A. A Hyperbolic Model

A study of 50 substituted phenols including either chlorine or bromine, and one or more small alkyl groups was reported with phenol coefficients, log PC, (Klarmann et al, 1933). A preliminary plot of log PC with ^1X revealed that the points did not exhibit a maximum value followed by declining values. Two equations that correlate well are:

$$\text{Log PC} = -5.6 + 2.00 \; ^1X - 0.11 \; (^1X)^2$$
$$r = 0.977, \; s = 0.20, \; N = 49, \; F = 474$$

$$\text{Log PC} = 6.31 - 21.41/^1X$$
$$r = 0.975, \; s = 0.20, \; N = 49, \; F = 921$$

The first equation, in two variable, describes a parabolic relationship with a maximum log PC value of 3.69 for $^1X = 9.09$. No molecules in the database have or exceed these maximal log PC or ^1X values. The second equation describing a hyperbolic relationship is statistically superior to the quadratic equation. The asymptotic value for this equation is a log PC of about 6.3.

It is clear that the data range does not permit the prediction of activity very far beyond the upper limit of the potency of the most active compound in the database. Extrapolation from the quadratic equation leads to predictions of declining activity beyond a certain value of ^1X. The hyperbolic equation leads to predictions of potency higher than the upper limit encountered in the database. The choice of equations makes a profound difference in the extrapolated predictions. A preliminary plotting of the data would reveal this limitation for extrapolative predictions.

B. A Quadratic Model

In another study on phenols from the work of E. G. Klarmann (1960), another nonlinear data set has been analyzed. A set of 34 phenols containing alkyl, alkoxy and halogen substituents was studied on the organism S. typhosa. A plot of the activity pC (-log of the phenol coefficient) against variables such as $^1x^v$, $^2x^v$ or the number of skeletal atoms reveals significant nonlinearity. The plots show a maximum in the activity with a significant number of compounds having activities beyond the maximum point. It appears that a quadratic form is appropriate in this case.

Use of a computerized routine to calculate regression for all possible pairs of variables indicates that quadratic models in $^1x^v$ and in $^2x^v$ give excellent results. The equation in $^1x^v$ and $(^1x^v)^2$ gives the same regression statistics as reported by Hansch and Fujita (1964) for π and π^2: $r = 0.921$, $s = 0.256$, $F = 86.3$, $n = 34$.

The quadratic model for $^2x^v$ is, however, even better:

$$pC = 3.828 \; ^2x^v - 0.583 \; (^2x^v)^2 - 4.590$$
$$r = 0.941, \; s = 0.222, \; F = 120.4, \; n = 34$$

The t values are large for both variables and the sequential F test indicates a very high significance for the squared term. In this case, the quadratic model appears to be very appropriate. The activity value at the maximum of the equation is 1.69, corresponding to a $^2X^V$ value of 3.283.

C. A Gaussian Model

Another non-linear equation was reported in a study of the QSAR of floral-scented odorants (Kier and Hall, 1977). The data reported as an odor similarity index, OS, to a standard substance (Amoore, 1970) was found to correlate closely with the ^OX connectivity index in a Gaussian relationship:

$$OS = 3.12 \ exp \ [-1.66(^OX - 9.51)^2] + 3.43$$
$$r = 0.959, \ S = 0.225, \ n = 16$$

This model was found to be superior to a quadratic equation describing a parabolic relationship. The Gaussian model describes an abrupt rise in the OS beyond a certain value with one value of ^OX being clearly delineated as describing the highest OS value. The abrupt decline from this maximum describes a marked departure from the ideal structure, leading to dramatically lower OS values.

5. Use of Additional Parameters as Equation Variables

A structural description of a molecule may not be complete with an ensemble of molecular connectivity indexes. Indeed, we have never claimed a complete encoding of all salient features in these indexes which influence a molecular property or a biological activity. In many cases, chi indexes give statistical quality approaching the precision of the data. In other cases, factors beyond the ability of molecular connectivity to describe have emerged as being important in a QSAR analysis.

Before discussing some of these non-coded properties, it is worth a few words to speak about the inclusion of properties as additional variables where the property is one which can itself be described by chi indexes. Two cases in point are the value of the partition coefficient, usually an octanol-water ratio, log P, and the molar refraction, MR. We have shown that both of these properties can be described with connectivity indexes. The inclusion of log P and/or MR in a regression analysis is, therefore, apt to lead to redundant terms which intercorrelate to a significant degree. Further, the inclusion of a property value such as log P or MR with structural chi indexes is not in harmony with the intention of finding the structure features which influence properties. If a property can be described with molecular connectivity, the chi indexes should be used exclusively.

A. Non-Coded Properties

Certain properties or structural aspects of molecules are less amenable to connectivity description by virtue of the fact that the property arises from a physical phenomenon associated with one part of the molecule, irrespective of the remainder of a molecule. The measure of an equilibrium property may be associated with a particular functional group and is significantly influenced by only the most proximate structural features. An aliphatic amine has a measured pKa due to the immediate environment. Atoms beyond two or three non-conjugated bond lengths are virtually silent in their influence. Properties due exclusively to a region of a molecule are not amenable to the usual description by connectivity indexes which are derived from the entire structure. This subject is considered in the last chapter.

Other cases in which chi indexes do not encode the salient structural features are structural or topological characteristics for which molecular connectivity and other structure descriptions are inadequate at the present time. This includes the encoding of information about cis-trans isomerism and symmetry. The inclusion of property values and indicator variables to describe non-encoded structural features have made up a number of studies in the literature. The discussion of some of these additional parameters follows.

B. Hammett Sigma Values

The contribution of a substituent group to the reactivity of a part of a molecule has been quantitated in a relative sense with the Hammett sigma value (1970). This is the ratio of a substituent contribution to a specified property, relative to the contribution of the substituent hydrogen. The sigma values express a regional influence in a molecule; hence, a whole-molecule index may be inappropriate to encode this effect. Inclusion of one of the many Hammett sigma values in a regression analysis against a property or biological activity expands the equation model possibilities. When found by regression analysis to be a structural factor, the Hammett sigma term lends itself to interpretation in a concise way.

An illustration of the contribution of the Hammett sigma value to a QSAR equation is found in a study of ring substituted benzyl alcohols and their relative abilities to inhibit the mold Aspergilus niger (Carter et al, 1958). The use of $^1X^v$ alone revealed a correlation of r = 0.890 with the potency, log 1/c (Kier and Hall, 1976). Inclusion of the Hammett sigma gave an improved equation: r = 0.937, s = 0.286. However, use of $^4X_p^v$ and σ gives even better results:

$$\log \ 1/c = 2.021 \ ^4X_p^v + 0.504 \ \sigma + 0.323$$
$$r = 0.959, \ s = 0.225, \ N = 19$$

The σ and $^4X_p^v$ terms are not correlated (r = 0.343); hence, independent information is conveyed by these terms. The meaningful contribution of to the model indicates a role for the substituent in contributing to the electronic structure of the ring and the hydroxy-methyl group. The $^4X_p^v$ index describes the contribution due to topology of the benzyl alcohol substituent.

C. Molecular Symmetry

Molecular Symmetry is a topological property characterizing the presence of atoms which correspond in type and position in space relative to a dividing line, plane or central point. The quantitation of this attribute has been suggested to be possible from calculations of the information content, negentropy, or redundancy of a molecule, Kier (1980b). All of these descriptors have their origins in the Shannon equation for information content (Shannon and Weaver, 1949):

$$i = -\Sigma \, p_j \log \, p_j \qquad (2)$$

where i is the information content per atom or the negentropy per atom, and p_j is the probability of selecting atom j from the collection of atoms comprising the molecule. Propane illustrates the calculation:

$$
\begin{array}{cccccccc}
 & & H^a & & H^b & & H^a & \\
 & & | & & | & & | & \\
H_a & - & C_c & - & C_d & - & C_c & - H_a \\
 & & | & & | & & | & \\
 & & H_a & & H_b & & H_a &
\end{array}
$$

It is apparent that the six hydrogens on the two methyl groups will map onto themselves; that is, they are each topologically equivalent to the other five methyl hydrogens. This is confirmed physically by the fact that all six respond identically to NMR analysis. All hydrogens in this set are labeled H_a. The methylene hydrogen atoms are not equivalent to the methyl hydrogens, but they are equivalent to each other. These comprise a second set, and the atoms are labeled H_b. The methyl carbons are topologically equivalent and are labeled C_c. Finally, the methylene carbon C_d comprises a fourth set and is unique.

We now compute the probabilities of random selection from among the eleven atoms in the molecule:

sets	(a)	(b)	(c)	(d)
multiplicity	6	2	2	1
selection probability	6/11	2/11	2/11	1/11

Table 4. Molecular negentropy and redundancy of isomeric heptanes.

Heptane	I	R
3-methyl hexane	25.219	0.195
2-methyl hexane	22.811	0.272
2,3-dimethyl pentane	22.584	0.279
hexane	19.426	0.379
2,2-dimethyl pentane	18.665	0.404
3,3-dimethyl pentane	17.768	0.432
2,2,3-trimethyl butane	16.029	0.488
3-ethyl pentane	15.200	0.515
2,4-dimethyl pentane	14.155	0.548

The information content per atom, (Eq. 2), is:

$$i = -[6/11 \log 6/11 + 2/11 \log 2/11 + 2/11 \log 2/11 + 1/11 \log 1/11]$$
$$i = 0.507$$

The information content of the molecule, I, for N = 11 atoms is:

$$I = iN = 5.582$$

Brillouin (1956) has introduced an alternative expression called redundancy, R, where

$$R = 1 - i/\log N$$

The values of I and R are shown for the heptane isomers in Table 4. Clearly, the ordering due to either index satisfies our intuition that the symmetry of the molecules is ranked. Applications of this index to biological QSAR have been published (Kier, 1980).

D. Indicator Variables

Circumstances arise where the presence or absence of a particular molecular fragment is a factor in the magnitude of a property or activity. The use of indicator variables for these attributes encodes the necessary information needed to evaluate these contributions to an equation model. One example illustrates this.

In a study on anesthetic gases, DiPaolo (1977) found it necessary to include a term describing the polarity of activated C-H bonds. In the general case:

$$A_2 - \overset{\overset{\displaystyle A_1}{|}}{\underset{\underset{\displaystyle A_3}{|}}{C}} - H$$

the variable for the hydrogen charge, Q_H, is approximated from the sum of electronegativity differences between each atom, A, and carbon, using the Pauling values. When this sum is greater than 1.0, the indicator variable for the C-H bond polarity, Q_H, is given a value of 0.10; when the sum is 0.5-1.0, $Q_H = 0.05$; when the sum is less than 0.5, $Q_H = 0.0$. The Q_H variable thus reflects an approximation of the charge on the hydrogen atom of the activated C-H moiety. The equation describing the structural contribution, $^0X^v$, and the electronic factor, Q_H, influencing the anesthetic potency, log 1/p, is:

$$\log 1/p = 0.548 \, {}^0X^v + 8.28 \, Q_H - 0.797$$
$$r = 0.982, \ s = 0.267, \ N = 14, \ F = 149$$

The interpretation of this indicator variable is clear since it was defined concisely. Activity is influenced by a polar C-H bond in a positive way. A subsequent study on anesthetic halocarbons confirmed the importance of this attribute using this same indicator variable (DiPaolo et al, 1979).

An indicator variable may also be used to merge two data sets in which the molecules in the two lists differ in some constant way. Hall and Kier (1975) combined alkanes and alcohols for a water solubility study. The indicator variable was set to 1 for alcohols and 0 for alkanes. The constant difference is presumed due to hydrogen bonding.

E. Other Physical Properties

In principal, any physical property which represents an effect of importance for a model may be used as a QSAR variable. It is important that the property have meaning in terms of the biological process and that it is not correlated with the chi indexes being used. One example is noted here and discussed in Chapter 7.

Richard and Kier (1980) analysed connectivity indexes plus a description of electron affinity of certain monoamine oxidase inhibitors using the polarographic half-wave reduction potential.

6. Use of Other Statistical Methods

Besides multiple linear regression there are other statistical methods which can be applied to QSAR problems using molecular connectivity indexes. In fact, any technique which requires a set of numerical variables may make use of chi indexes as the variables. As shown earlier, additional variables of several types may be used to supplement the structure descriptors in the chi index set.

A. Total Response Surface Optimization

As indicated in an earlier section, the relation between biological activity and structure is sometimes nonlinear. It is not expected that activity will increase indefinitely as molecules increase in size or other characteristics. Often, when a single structure variable is used, the nonlinear relation is given by the simple quadratic equation. When the activity depends quadratically on two variables, the mathematical situation becomes more complicated. A cross term in the two variables must be used in addition to the linear and squared terms for a complete description. This makes a total of five variables to be handled with multiple linear regression. It may well be that there are insufficient observations in the data set to permit reliable statistical estimations for the six parameters associated with five variables. The following discussion shows how this problem may be approached in a general fashion and how connectivity indexes may be used in a specific example.

Some statistical systems have specific procedures which may be helpful in this analysis; however, standard multiple linear regression methods are all that is necessary. Authors such as Mager have also discussed the mathematical background (1980) and pharmacological applications of this approach (1982).

B. Size and Electronic Effects

To illustrate the response surface approach, a specific example will be used. Mager (1982) has reported the neurotoxicity of 21 phosphofluoridates, phosphonofluoridates and phosphorodiamidofluoridates. There are cyclic and noncyclic alkyl portions of the esters and amides and one aromatic substituent. The activity is reported as mg/kg i.m. to produce ataxia in adult hens. The amounts were put on a molar basis and the dependent variable taken as the negative logarithm. These pD values range from 3.2 to 5.92. (See Table 5.)

Preliminary examination of the data set shows a pronounced nonlinear relationship between pD and variables such as ^1X, $^1X^v$ or number of skeletal atoms. Regression against any one of the variables in a quadratic model is, however, not entirely adequate.

TABLE 5.   Neurotoxicity of fluorophosphates with molecular
            connectivity indexes and transformed indexes.

ID	Substituents (R1,R2)	a) SUM	b) DIFF	c) Z_1	d) Z_2	Obs	e) Calc
1	Di-(propylamino)	8.934	1.309	-1.794	0.813	5.86	5.67
2	Di-(butylamino)	10.934	1.309	0.206	0.813	5.92	5.81
3	Di-propoxy	8.681	1.561	-2.047	1.066	5.66	5.49
4	Di-butoxy	10.681	1.561	-0.047	1.066	5.63	5.68
5	Di-isopropoxy	8.182	1.484	-2.546	0.988	5.57	5.44
6	Di-secpentoxy	12.334	1.484	1.606	0.988	5.43	5.61
7	Di-(ethylamino)	6.934	1.309	-3.794	0.813	5.11	5.19
8	Di-pentoxy	12.681	1.561	1.953	1.066	5.26	5.51
9	N,N-dimethyl, ethoxy	6.836	1.172	-3.892	0.676	5.00	5.22
10	Di-ethoxy	6.681	1.561	-4.047	1.066	5.07	4.97
11	Di-cyclohexyloxy	14.829	1.484	4.101	0.988	5.20	4.99
12	Isopropoxy, methyl	5.772	1.061	-4.956	0.565	4.94	4.85
13	Ethoxy, methyl	5.022	1.099	-5.707	0.604	4.62	4.49
14	N,N'-dimethyl, methoxy	5.401	1.607	-5.327	1.111	4.67	4.42
15	Di-(cyclohexylamino)	15.058	1.255	4.330	0.759	4.72	5.03
16	Di-(methylamino)	4.813	1.430	-5.916	0.934	4.09	4.24
17	Dimethoxy	4.506	1.737	-6.222	1.241	4.03	3.88
18	Di-(2-methylphenylamino)	14.824	3.132	4.096	2.636	3.23	3.27
19	Isopropoxy, ethyl	6.844	1.111	-3.885	0.615	5.29	5.24
20	Isopropoxy, methyl	7.432	1.523	-3.297	1.027	5.07	5.23
21	Hydroxy, methyl	2.992	1.008	-7.737	0.513	3.20	3.34

a)   SUM $= Y_1 = {}^1X + {}^1X^v$
b)   DIFF $= Y_2 = {}^1X - {}^1X^v$
c) $Z_1 = Y_1 - Y_1 \text{(max)} = Y_1 - 11.1117$
d) $Z_2 = Y_2 - Y_2 \text{(max)} = Y_2 + 0.4315$
e)   Calculated from final regression equation, eqn. 4.

A more general quadratic model based on two variables is needed. Mager used π and MR values. The general form of the equation is as follows:

$$pC = b_1 x_1^2 + a_1 x_1 + b_2 x_2^2 + a_2 x_2 + c x_1 x_2 + d \qquad (3)$$

Using ^1X and $^1X^V$ as the two variables, an excellent regression result is obtained:

$$pD = -0.2350(^1X)^2 + 1.2485\ ^1X - 0.1700(^1X^V)^2$$
$$+ 0.7955\ ^1X^V + 0.2186\ ^1X^1X^V + 0.6605 \qquad (4)$$
$$r = 0.981,\ s = 0.17,\ F = 77.1,\ n = 21$$

See Table 5 for the list of compounds and computed results.

Before proceeding with the response surface analysis, a comment on interpretation is important. What information of significance is conveyed to us by the chi indexes used in this example? Elements of both molecular size and electronic effects are contained in $^1X^V$, whereas ^1X refers primarily to molecular size since information about heteroatoms is excluded. It is possible to use a simple transformation of these variables to effect a separation of the size and electronic effects. This transformation will be introduced at this point and the resulting equation will be subjected to the analysis of the general quadratic surface, as is done in response surface analysis. The use of these transformed variables is not necessary to the response surface analysis.

Define new variables:

$$Y_1 = {}^1X + {}^1X^V \qquad (5)$$
$$Y_2 = {}^1X - {}^1X^V \qquad (6)$$

If we consider molecules such as alkyl alcohols, halides, amides, etc., it can readily be shown that $^1X^V$ can be dissected into a term arising from the functional group, S_{fg}, and the rest of $^1X^V$ which is based on the remaining alkyl portion of the molecule, S_{alk}. This partition is possible because of the additive nature of the chi index.

In the ^1X index, on the other hand, all the terms are calculated as if the molecule were an alkane. Thus, ^1X can be written as two terms: S_{ag}, for the skeletal portion of the functional group, and S_{alk} for the remainder of the molecule. The term S_{alk} is, of course, the same for the two indexes. Using the sum and difference variables defined above,

$$Y_1 = {}^1X + {}^1X^v = (S_{ag} + S_{alk}) + (S_{fg} + S_{alk})$$
$$Y_1 = 2 S_{alk} + (S_{ag} + S_{fg})$$

and

$$Y_2 = S_{ag} - S_{fg}$$

Two effects can be summarized for these transformed variables Y_1 and Y_2.

i. The Sum Variable Y_1

In the sum variable Y_1, the common portion of the two indexes is emphasized from multiplication by 2, and the functional group portion S_{fg} is augmented by S_{ag}. Since all these terms carry information about the size of the molecule, the sum variable represents an aspect of molecular size. The heteroatom contribution to size is carried through δ^v in S_{fg} and the extent of the skeleton is represented by S_{alk} and S_{ag}. See the discussion on volume and the van der Waals b constant in Chapter 2, section 6B.

ii. The Difference Variable Y_2

In marked contrast, the difference variable carries an entirely different type of information. The terms for the saturated portion of the molecule drop out entirely. Further, in Y_2 the functional group is represented by the difference $S_{ag} - S_{fg}$. This difference further accentuates the heteroatom contribution.

In terms of molecular electronic structure, the difference between functional groups and alkyl portions is in the type of the bonds. Electrons are found only in sigma orbitals in the alkyl group, whereas electrons are also in pi and lone pair orbitals in functional groups. The difference variable Y_2 is a measure of the electronic contribution of electrons in pi and lone pair orbitals.

The sum variable Y_1 emphasizes the whole molecular skeleton, including functional groups. This variable, based on a summation of all skeletal connections and reflecting the varying contributions of heteroatoms, is expected to relate to molecular size.

The difference variable Y_2 emphasizes the nonsigma electrons; that is, the electrons which have a major influence on electronic properties. For singly bonded nitrogen, oxygen, or fluorine, Y_2 relates to lone pair electrons. For doubly bonded oxygen, nitrogen, and phorphorus, Y_2 relates to pi electrons. For aromatic rings, Y_2 represents the delocalized pi electrons. These two variables permit a factoring of information into effects related to molecular size and to electronic structure.

It should be pointed out here that the transformed variables Y_1 and Y_2 also possess a very useful mathematical property. Y_1 and Y_2 are orthogonal to each other. This characteristic is very useful in eliminating collinearities which often arise in data sets. The transformation to the sum and difference variables is related to using the eigenvectors from a principal component analysis. A similar transformation can be used when physical properties are used as variables, such as log P and MR (molar refraction), as was shown by Mager in his analysis of the neurotoxicity data set; however, the transformed variables, linear combination of log P and MR, have no particular physical significance.

The biological activity can be regressed against the transformed variables Y_1 and Y_2 in the full quadratic model with the same statistical result as eqn. (4).

$$pD = -0.04557Y_1^2 + 0.9890Y_1 - 0.2469Y_2^2$$
$$+ 0.4883Y_2 - 0.02271Y_1Y_2 + 0.5395$$
$$r = 0.981, \ s = 0.169, \ F = 77.1, \ n = 21$$

From the mathematical perspective, this equation represents a parabolic surface with a maximum. The response surface analysis may now be performed on this equation. The equation may be simplified by moving the origin of the coordinate system to the maximum point in the overall surface. From elementary calculus, this point corresponds to the derivatives being zero. The values of Y_1 and Y_2 at the maximum are given as:

$$Y_1 \ (max) = (2a_1b_2 - a_2c)/(c^2 - 4b_1b_2)$$

$$Y_2 \ (max) = (2a_2b_1 - a_1c)/(c^2 - 4b_1b_2)$$

For the present case,

$$Y_1 \ (max) = 11.1117 \qquad\qquad Y_2 \ (max) = 0.4315$$

The new variables in the transformed coordinate system are:

$$Z_1 = Y_1 - Y_1 \ (max) \qquad\qquad Z_2 = Y_2 - Y_2 \ (max)$$

When this substitution is made, the linear terms in the equation drop out. The remaining equation in Z, then, has only three variables. When subjected to regression analysis, the following equation results with the same level of correlation coefficient but with higher F value because of the smaller number of variables.

$$pD = -0.04662 \ (Z_1)^2 - 0.1559 \ (Z_2)^2 - 0.03249 \ Z_1Z_2 + 6.290 \qquad (7)$$
$$r = 0.981, \ s = 0.159, \ F = 146, \ n = 21$$

Table 5 gives the compound identifications, the numerical values of the sum and difference variables along with the Z variables, the observed, calculated and residual values. The results clearly indicate the quality of the model. The largest residual is for the only cyclic aliphatic substituent, no. 11. There are no residuals greater than twice the standard deviation.

The regression model can now be analyzed in terms of the sum and difference variables. As shown in Table 5, the sum variable is much larger than the difference variable, as can be understood from its definition. Further, the Y_1 variable spans a wider range of values (2.992 to 15.058) than does the difference variable (1.008 to 3.132). Y_2 is nearly constant except for the two extreme values: 3.132 for no. 18, and 1.008 for no. 21. No. 18 is the only compound with an aromatic substituent, and no. 21 is the only phosphinic acid. The electronic effects for this data set represented by Y_2 do not vary nearly as much as the size effect represented by Y_1.

It can be further shown that on a plot of $^1X^V$ versus ^1X, most of the compounds tend to fall along a region near to the line $^1X^V = {}^1X$. The two significant exceptions are, of course, nos. 18 and 21. Further, those with direct alkyl substitution on the phosphorus fall in an area near $^1X - {}^1X^V = 1.1$, while for esters and amides, $^1X - {}^1X^V = 1.25$. It follows that a purely size parameter would explain most but not all of the data variation. It should be noted that the two compounds with the most electronic difference, nos. 18 and 21, are very well predicted by the model.

From the regression model, eqn. (7), the maximum toxicity and variables at the maximum toxicity may easily be obtained since $Z_1 = Z_2 = 0$ represents the maximum.

$$pD_{max} = 6.290$$

$$Y_1 \text{ (max)} = 11.1117 \qquad Y_2 \text{ (max)} = -0.4315$$

From the definition of Y and Z, the values of ^1X and $^1X^V$ at the maximum are obtained:

$$^1X \text{ (max)} = 5.3421 \qquad \text{and} \qquad {}^1X^V \text{ (max)} = 5.7743$$

It is observed that no compound in the data set corresponds to these values, although no. 2 is perhaps the closest. If one wishes to produce compounds with lower neurotoxicity, then compounds should be selected with ^1X and $^1X^V$ values far from the maximum values quoted above. One can also be guided in terms of molecular electronic structure by looking for molecules with sum and difference variables Y_1 and Y_2 very different from those given above. Greater size resulting from increased alkyl portions or smaller molecules with greater electronic contribution from heteroatoms would appear to create less toxic compounds. Alternatively introducing more size along with much greater contribution from non-sigma electrons would place a molecule away from the maximum. This case is illustrated by the low toxicity of no. 18.

Compounds with maximum activity will have $Z_1 = Z_2 = 0$; $Y_1 = Y_1$ (max) and $Y_2 = Y_2$ (max). The principal molecular aspect to be optimized for these molecules is electronic structure. For these molecules, $Y_2 = 0.4315$ or the $^1X^V$ index should be near to the value of ^1X. The simplest way to accomplish this is to decrease the number of heteroatoms. For example, the -NH- or -0- groups could be changed to $-CH_2-$ groups.

This example shows how the response surface optimization (parabolic surface analysis) techniques can be applied to a model based on chi molecular structure indexes. Whether one also makes use of the sum and difference transformation is quite independent of this technique. In this particular case the ^1X and $^1X^V$ variables were used. Other data sets have been analyzed using the $^0X, ^0X^V$ or $^2X, ^2X^V$ pairs of variables. Guidance in the selection of such variables is discussed in the opening section of this chapter.

C. Discriminant Analysis

Discriminant analysis is a statistical method for differentiating between classes of objects. The method has been recognized as potentially useful in QSAR (Martin, 1974) but has only recently received much attention (Dove, Franke et al, 1978) (Dunn, Wold and

Martin, 1978) (Henry and Block, 1979). Several studies have shown that discriminant analysis may be performed using connectivity indexes (Henry and Block, 1979, 1980) (Kier, 1980c) (Stupor and Jurs, 1978). The chi indexes serve as the variables upon which discriminant functions or classification is based.

In one form of analysis, the discriminant method develops a linear combination of variables:

$$Y = a_1 x_1 + a_2 x_2 + \text{---} + a_n x_n$$

which separates the classes of objects with as little overlap as possible. The discriminant function is a surface (line, plane etc.) in n-dimensional space, computed so as to lie between and divide the classes of molecules. The coefficients a_i are determined so as to maximize the distance (in the n-dimensional space defined by the x_i variables) between molecules in different classes while minimizing the distance between molecules in the same class. A critical value Y^* is computed to lie between the classes so that when $Y > Y^*$, the object is placed in one class and when $Y > Y^*$, the object is placed in the other class. This form of analysis is particularly useful when there are only two classes.

In another form of discriminant analysis, each object is represented by a point in the n-dimensional space of the independent variables used. Classification is based on the generalized distance between objects in the space. Each observation is placed in the class from which it has the smallest generalized squared distance. For a specific example, consider a data set determined by Dove et al (1979) for a series of 22 toluenesulfonylureas and thioureas. The molecules in the series are substituted in two positions: in the para position on the toluene ring and on the terminal $-NH_2$ in the urea. Further, several compounds are thioureas. (See Table 8.)

The compounds were tested on rats for blood sugar level control. Nine compounds were found to be hyperglycemic and assigned to class 1; eight were found to be inactive and assigned to class 2;

five were assigned to class 3 as hypoglycemic. Connectivity indexes were calculated through the sixth order for the set of 22 molecules.

Since the substituents R_1 and R_2 occupy sites at opposite ends of the molecule, it would not be surprising if these groups exert independent influences on the activities. For this reason, chi indexes were also calculated for truncated portions of the molecule. For R_1, para-substituted xylene was used. For R_2, N-substituted urea (or thiourea) was used. ^0X, $^0X^V$, ^1X and $^1X^V$ were stored in the data file for both of these truncated molecules.

Preliminary results indicated that $^1X^V$ for both R_1 and R_2 are important for good classification. Further, the long path variable ^6X_p is also important. This variable may encode information about R_2 variation on the urea and the variation of the carbonyl group to a thiocarbonyl.

Using the three variables $^1X^V(R_1)$, $^1X^V(R_2)$ and ^6X_p, good classification results are obtained: 18 of 21 are classified into the correct classes as shown in Table 6. All five of the hypoglycemic compounds are correctly classified (Class 3). Only one inactive compound is incorrectly classified; it was placed in Class 3. Two of the hyperglycemic compounds were misclassfied, one as inactive and one as hypoglycemic.

It may be possible to improve the classification statistics by increasing the number of variables used. For example, an indicator variable may be introduced to distinguish the thioureas from the ureas. In this case, the addition of an indicator variable drops the number misclassified to 2. Number 4, a thiourea, is properly classified as hyperglycemic. Depending upon the significance of this result and the purpose of the study, it may be deemed useful to include the thio/oxy indicator variable.

The classification analysis may also be done on this data set as three two-way analyses. In this approach, a linear discriminant function is determined for each pair of classes. This approach permits the separate analysis of each pair of classes with the possibility of detecting effects which are not readily apparent in the overall approach.

TABLE 6.   Classification results for blood sugar level using the
            generalized distance method.

NUMBER OF OBSERVATIONS AND PERCENTS CLASSIFIED INTO CLASS

Into Class

		1	2	3	Total
	1	7	1	1	9
		77.78	11.11	11.11	100.00
From					
	2	0	7	1	8
Class		0.00	87.50	12.50	100.00
	3	0	0	5	5
		0.00	0.00	100.00	100.00

POSTERIOR PROBABILITY: MISCLASSIFIED OBSERVATIONS

Obs	from Class	Classified into Class	Probability 1	2	3
4	1	3*	0.1747	0.0003	0.8250
9	1	2*	0.2173	0.7820	0.0007
10	2	3*	0.0571	0.1276	0.8153

*   Misclassified Observation

TABLE 7.   Classification of sulfonylureas into hyperglycemic and
           hypoglycemic activity using the discriminant function
           method.

I. HYPERGLYCEMIC/HYPOGLYCEMIC

Discriminant Function	T^2	F	P	Classification	
$-15.1\ {}^6X_p + 6.66\ {}^1X\ (R_1)$	25.9	12.0	.001	14/14	100.0%
$1.7\ {}^1X^v\ (R_1)$	5.1	5.1	.05	9/14	69.2%

II. HYPOGLYCEMIC/NON-ACTIVE

$-37.2\ {}^6X_p^v + 5.25\ {}^1X^v\ (R_1)$	33.5	15.4	.001	13/13	100.0%
$-13.0\ {}^6X_p^v$	6.2	6.2	.025	11/13	84.6%

III. HYPERGLYCEMIC/NON-ACTIVE

$-1.13\ {}^1X^v$	6.6	6.6	.02	14/17	82.3%

Table 7 summarizes the statistics for the three discriminant
analyses. Table 8 gives the list of compounds and the classifications
for each pair of analyses. In all three cases excellent results are
obtained. Case III in Table 7 is the least satisfactory, although
the 82.3% is a useful result. This result parallels that from the
three-way analysis in that the hyperglycemic compounds are the
most difficult to classify. Further, compound 9 is consistently

TABLE 8.   Classification of sulfonylureas by class.

$R_1 - PH - SO_2 - NH - CX - NH - R_2$

| | R_1 | R_2 | X | Classification* | | | |
				EXP	1/3	2/3	1/2
1	CH_3O	CH_3	O	1	1		1
2	CH_3O	C_2H_5	O	1	1		1
3	CH_3O	C_3H_7	O	1	1		1
4	CH_3O	C_3H_7	S	1	1		1
5	CH_3O	H	O	1	1		1
6	C_2H_5O	H	O	1	1		1
7	C_3H_7O	C_4H_9	S	1	1		2
8	C_4H_9O	CH_3	O	1	1		1
9	C_4H_9O	C_4H_9	O	1	1		2
10	CH_3O	C_4H_9	O	2		2	1
11	CH_3O	CH_2Ph	O	2		2	2
12	C_2H_5O	C_4H_9	O	2		2	2
13	C_3H_9O	C_4H_9	O	2		2	2
14	C_4H_9O	CH_3	S	2		2	2
15	$C_5H_{11}O$	C_4H_9	O	2		2	2
16	$C_5H_{11}O$	C_4H_9	S	2		2	2
17	CH_3CONH	C_4H_9	O	2		2	2
18	CH_3O	CH_2Ph	S	3	3	3	
19	C_2H_5O	C_4H_9	S	3	3	3	
20	CH_3CONH	C_4H_9	S	3	3	3	
21	CH_3	C_4H_9	O	3	3	3	
22	CH_3	C_4H_9	S	3	3	3	

*Class 1: Hyperglycemic   Class 2: Non Active   Class 3: Hypoglycemic

misclassified. It should be noted that a whole molecule index is used in this case. The two substituent indexes did not give highly significant results.

By contrast in Cases I and II the $^1X^V$ substituent index is necessary but only for the R_1 group. These results indicate a significant role for the substituents on the toluene ring. In addition, the ^6X_p index is necessary in case I and makes 100% classification possible. In case II the corresponding valence index is necessary. This may indicate a significant role for the thio-substitution in relation to R_2 substituents. A more detailed subgraph analysis may be helpful here. (See section 3 for an example subgraph analysis in another QSAR problem.)

7. Conclusions

The molecular connectivity method for QSAR is designed to provide numerical indexes of molecular structure. As shown in Chapters 1, 3 and 4, many aspects of molecular structure are encoded in the chi indexes. Because of the wide variation of structural features encountered in molecules of biological interest, many different chi indexes are possible. The set of simple indexes emphasizes skeletal arrangement including branching and cyclization. The valence chi indexes contain information about the specific nature of the hetero-atoms in the molecule. Because chemical structure features in molecules and the corresponding structure information are not necessarily independent, the chi indexes are also not independent. For example, both a tertiary amine and a secondary alcohol imply a three-way skeletal branch point. The large number of connectivity indexes and their intercorrelations require careful attention to detail in their use in statistical models. This is not a difficult task as shown in this chapter.

Chapters 5 and 6 are written to provide guidelines and examples for the use of connectivity indexes in QSAR models. The process is essentially the same as for traditional SAR studies. The result, however, is that the interpretation of the resulting QSAR model may be done directly in terms of the structure of the molecules themselves. It is not necessary to use intermediaries such as properties. These first six chapters have shown how to establish the direct link between molecular structure and biological activity. Chapter 7 is devoted to selected examples of application of molecular connectivity to QSAR problems of biological interest.

References

Amoore, J. E. (1970). Molecular Basis of Odor, C. C. Thomas, Springfield, Ill.

Berger, F. M., Hubbard, C. V. and Ludwig, B. J. (1953). Antimicrobial action of certain glycerol ethers and related compounds. Appl. Microbiol. 1, 146-149.

Brillouin, L. (1962). Science and Information Theory, Academic Press, New York.

Carter, D. V., Charlton, P. T., Fenton, A. H., Housey, J. R. and Lessel, B. (1958). The preparation and the antibacterial and antifungal properties of some substituted benzyl alcohols. J. Pharm. Pharmacol. 10 Suppl., 149T.

DiPaolo, T., Kier, L. B. and Hall, L. H. (1977). Molecular connectivity and structure-activity relationship of general anesthetics. Molec. Pharmacol., 13, 31-37.

DiPaolo, T., Kier, L. B. and Hall, L. H. (1979). Molecular connectivity study of halocarbon anesthetics. J. Pharm. Sci., 68, 39-42.

Dove, S., Franke, R., Mndshojan, O. L., Schuljer, W. A. and Chashakjan, L. W. (1979). Discriminant analytical investigation on the structural dependence of hyperglycemic and hypoglycemic activity in a series of substituted o-toluenesulfonylureas and o-toluenesulfonylthioureas. J. Med. Chem., 22, 90-95.

Dunn, W. J., Wold, S. and Martin, Y. C. (1978). Structure activity study of beta-adrenergic agents using the SIMCA method of pattern recognition. J. Med. Chem., 21, 922-930.

Glennon, R. A. and Kier, L. B. (1978a). LSD analogs as serotonin antagonists: A molecular connectivity SAR analysis. Eur. J. Med. Chem., 13, 219-223.

Hall, L. H., Kier, L. B. and Murray, W. J. (1975). Molecular connectivity II: Relationship to water solubility and boiling point. J. Pharm. Sci., 64, 1974-1977.

Hall, L. H. and Kier, L. B. (1978a). Molecular connectivity and substructure analysis. J. Pharm. Sci., 67, 1743-1747.

Hall, L. H. and Kier, L. B. (1978b). A comparative analysis of molecular connectivity: Hansch, Free-Wilson and DARC-PELCO methods in the SAR of halogenated phenols. Eur, J. Med. Chem., 13, 89-92.

Hammett, L. D. (1970). Physical Organic Chemistry, 2nd Ed., McGraw-Hill, New York.

Hansch, C. and Fujita, T. (1964). Pi rho sigma analysis: A method for the correlation of biological activity and chemical structure. J. Am. Chem. Soc., 86, 1616-1626.

Henry, D. R. and Block, J. H. (1979). Classification of drugs by discriminant analysis using fragment molecular connectivity values. J. Med. Chem., 22, 465-472.

Henry, D. R. and Block, J. H. (1980). Steroid classification by discriminant analysis using fragment molecular connectivity. Eur. J. Med. Chem., 15, 133-138.

Kier, L. B. and Hall. L. H. (1976). Molecular Connectivity in Chemistry and Drug Research, p. 211, Academic Press, New York.

Kier, L. B., DiPaolo, T. and Hall, L. H. (1977). Structure-activity studies on odor molecules using molecular connectivity. J. Theor. Biol., 67, 585-595.

Kier, L. B. (1980a). Structural information from molecular connectivity XPC4 index. J. Pharm. Sci., 69, 1034-1039.

Kier, L. B. (1980b). Use of molecular negentropy to encode structure governing biological activity. J. Pharm. Sci., 69, 807-810.

Kier, L. B. (1980c). Molecular structure influencing either a sweet or bitter taste among aldoximes. J. Pharm. Sci., 69, 416-419.

Kier, L. B. and Hall, L. H. (1983). General definition of valence delta values for molecular connectivity. J. Pharm. Sci., 72, 1170-1173.

Klarmann, E., Shternov V. A. and Gates, L. W. (1933). Alkyl derivatives of halophenols and their bactericidal action. J. Am. Chem. Soc., 55, 2576-2589.

Klarman, E. in Burger, A. (1960). Medicinal chemistry, 2nd Ed. Interscience Publishers, Inc., New York, p. 1123.

Mager, P. P. (1980). The MASCA model of pharmacochemistry, in E. J. Ariens (ed), Drug Design. Academic Press, New York, Vol IX, pp. 187-236, Vol X, pp. 343-401.

Mager, P. P. (1982). Structure-neurotoxicity relationships applied to organophosphorous pesticides. Tox. Lett., 11, 67-71.

Martin, Y. C., Holland, J. B. Jarbol, C. H. and Plotnikoff, J. (1974). Discriminant analysis of the relationship between physical properties and the inhibition of monoamine oxidase. J. Med. Chem., 17, 409-413.

Richard, A. J. and Kier. L. B. (1980). SAR analysis of hydrazide monoamine oxidase inhibitors using molecular connectivity. J. Pharm. Sci., 69, 124-125.

Shannon, C. E. and Weaver, W. (1949). The Mathematical Theory of Communication. University of Illinois Press, Urbanna, Ill.

Stupor, A. J. and Jurs, P. C. (1978). SAR studies of barbiturates using pattern recognition techniques. J. Pharm. Sci., 67 745-751.

CHAPTER 7

Applications
to Drug Studies

Molecular connectivity has been extensively used in quantitative structure activity relationship (QSAR) studies on series of biologically active molecules. The usual practice has been to calculate a number of connectivity indexes for each molecule in a series and then, through multiple linear regression analyses, find the best equation or equations in terms of correlation with a biological activity. The objectives of such an analysis fall into two categories: a) to find structural features influencing activity, or b) find an equation model which can be used to predict more active candidate molecules.

The critical feature of analyses using molecular connectivity is the lucid interpretation of equation variables as descriptions of molecular fragments. Indeed the selection of the "best" equation from among several with comparable statistics may often be based on the ease with which a structural description can be made. The ability to visualize the information encoded in each term of a regression variable is a powerful factor in the use of molecular connectivity for QSAR analyses. The second feature which makes this method so attractive is the great ease with which it can be employed. The only input to a computer program is the connection matrix and the atom identities.

1. Selection of Data for QSAR Analyses

The selection of data for QSAR analyses may well be the most difficult part of any study. A good correlation with poor data lacks meaning, but more seriously, it can convey a false sense of accomplishment which may escape the casual reader. It is not our intention to discuss this subject thoroughly, but to summarize two important points about data selection.

The best data for analysis is derived from measured responses from several doses. This permits the development of a profile of response beginning with a dose to produce an induction through the revelation of a maximum or asymptotic response. A measurement of a response from a single dose or a fixed dose for several compounds may result in identical values when in fact the dose used may be in the maximum zone for all compounds. This does not reveal the lower dose effects which may differ significantly among compounds tested. Usually the half maximal dose is used, expressed as a log of the molar concentration, LC_{50}.

Potency range is important to the statistical significance of any QSAR analysis. It is hard to establish a firm criterion for an activity range in any series under study; however, experience suggests a range of 2 log units as minimal for the LC_{50} values. If biological data is at hand with high precision, say ± 5%, then a somewhat narrower range of LC_{50} values may be acceptable. A thorough study should include some very weakly active or inactive compounds.

Several examples of QSAR studies have been selected for discussion in the following section. Each has certain unique features which provide the reader with insight into the capabilities and limitations of molecular connectivity. In each case we omit details of the biological testing method and focus on the calculations and particularly the interpretation of the results.

2. Study of Ecotoxicological Behavior

A recent study by Koch (1983) on the ecotoxicological behavior of environmental pollutants considered a list of 44 compounds. The sorption coefficient, log BS, was available for 18 compounds; the bioconcentration factor, log BCF, available for 21 compounds; and the guppy test toxicity, LC_{50}, for 31 compounds. Using the $^1\chi^v$ index, Koch reported three QSAR equations for the measured properties:

$$\log LC_{50} = 5.582 - 1.192\,^1\chi^v \quad , \quad r = 0.903 \quad (1)$$
$$\log BCF = 0.147 + 0.789\,^1\chi^v \quad , \quad r = 0.957 \quad (2)$$
$$\log BS = 0.445 + 0.673\,^1\chi^v \quad , \quad r = 0.974 \quad (3)$$

The best correlation, eqn. (3), relates the sorption to the structure encoded by $^1\chi^v$. This property is associated with the ability of a molecule to bind in a non-specific way to another molecule or to cell surfaces. This property may be viewed as an initial phenomenon in which a molecule participates, leading to a biological response. If the sorption event is the rate limiting step in a chain of events, we would expect that the bioconcentration measurement, a subsequent event, would be less well correlated with the same index, but still correlated well enough to reflect its significance in the overall process. This is the case in Koch's study. The correlation of log BCF, eqn. (2), is lower but still quite good. Finally the toxicity relation, eqn. (1), is lower in quality yet good enough to reflect its dependence upon $^1\chi^v$ and the two preceding events.

The three equations depict a sequence of events beginning with the most important, non-specific binding. This in turn influences absorption and bioconcentration. Finally the measured LC_{50} is dependent upon the absorbed molecule. The equations permit reasonable speculation on the mechanism exhibited by the compounds in the list. The $^1\chi^v$ index satisfactorily describes the structural attributes influencing each event; however, the actual equations are each different from the others. This is reasonable since the three events modeled are significantly different in terms of molecular interactions.

3. The QSAR of Flavor Threshold

In a series of papers, Gardner (1979) has studied the QSAR of the flavor constituents of beer. One facet of this study was the attempt to model the QSAR of the flavor threshold of beer constituents with molecular connectivity. The flavor threshold, T, is the minimum concentration in moles, needed to evoke a perception, as judged by panelists. The value, log (1/T), was measured for several classes of constituents including alcohols, ketones, aldehydes, esters and acids.

Gardner focused attention on equations modeling individual classes of flavor constituents. The studies considered two general equations and used only the $^1X^v$ parameter. The general equations are:

$$\log\ (1/T)\ =\ a(^1X^v)^b \tag{4}$$
$$\log\ (1/T)\ =\ a\,^1X^v + b(^1X^v)^2 + c \tag{5}$$

Examining Gardner's results for aliphatic alcohols, aldehydes and ketones, using both eqn. (4) and eqn. (5), the results are statistically quite good (see Table 1).

Both general equations are sufficiently robust to permit predictions by interpolation. A problem arises when it is of interest to extrapolate beyond the data base and make predictions about the flavor threshold. Further, the two equations are in serious conflict as far as a mechanistic interpretation of the QSAR models portrayed. From the coefficient, b, in the power equations, the generalization can be made that this model predicts an increasing threshold of taste as the molecules in each series increase in size. This interpretation satisfies our intuition that increasing size in a series, results in a lower volatility and reduced ability to stimulate taste on odor

TABLE 1.   Constants and statistical data for threshold
            concentration and $^1\chi^v$.

$$\log (1/T) = a(^1\chi^v)^b$$

compound series	a	b	c	r	s	n
alcohols	1.107	1.135	–	0.938	0.117	25
aldehydes	3.429	0.445	–	0.959		16
ketones	2.038	0.649	–	0.940		26

$$\log (1/T) = a\,^1\chi^v + b(^1\chi^v)^2 + c$$

	a	b	c	r	s	n
alcohols	2.866	−0.255	−1.843	0.951	0.623	25
aldehydes	1.326	−0.063	2.109	0.935	0.604	16
ketones	1.766	−0.127	0.113	0.944	0.382	26

receptors. In contrast, the parabolic equations, though they are as good if not better statistically, predict a very unsatisfying consequence of increased size. The model describes a decreasing taste sensitivity up to a certain size. Beyond that, there is predicted an increasing taste sensitivity so that a ketone of say 20 carbon atoms would evoke a taste perception equivalent to that of 7 or 8 carbon atoms. This certainly does not mirror reality.

Gardner recognized this dilemma since he has looked at multi-term connectivity equations to obtain even better QSAR models for one series of compounds. This kind of a dilemma can be prevented by examining just where the existing data falls in a plot of log (1/T) versus $^1\chi^v$. Figure 1, showing the log (1/T) for ketones versus

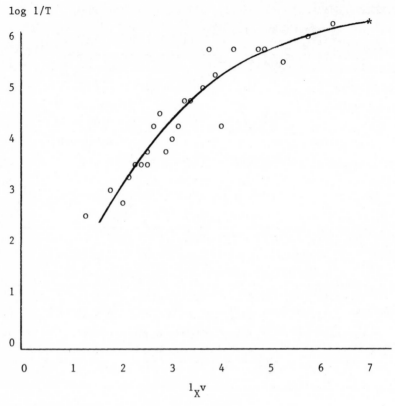

FIGURE 1. log (1/T) (Taste threshold) vs. $^1\chi^v$

$^1\chi^v$, reveals that no observations of log (1/T) fall beyond the maximum value of the parabola, shown as the starred point on the curve. Since the quadratic equation in two instances is somewhat better than the power curve, Table 1, it must be accepted as a good representation of the relationship within a limited range of data. Further QSAR analyses may reveal other, superior equation models with physical significance over a wider range of molecular size. Thus an inverse relationship with $^1\chi^v$ would portray an asymptotic relationship with some limiting value of log 1/T. A bilinear model would also mirror reality. Fortunately in this study, the molecules of very great length are not encountered, hence, the necessity to predict much beyond the size in the data base is not a factor. Nevertheless, a realistic equation model should always be sought.

4. QSAR of General Anesthetics

DiPaolo (1978) has analyzed the QSAR of hydrocarbons, ethers and ketones as general anesthetics. The effective concentration of compound, c, was expressed as log (1/c). The experimental standard error, expressed in this term, is reported to be 0.17. The data is shown in Table 2. The best equation was found to be:

$$-\log (1/c) = \frac{8.539}{^1X} + 1.487\,^4X_p^v - 2.895 \qquad (6)$$

$$r = 0.943, \quad s = 0.17, \quad n = 27, \quad F = 96.5$$

The equation accounts for 89% of the variance in log (1/c) and the standard error is at the level of the experimental error. The statistics reveal that this equation is as good as can be expected from this quality of data.

The interpretation of the structural information contained in the equation can be approached in several ways. It is instructive to find what is the relationship between the potency and the ^1X index in an initial analysis. Figure 2 reveals several facts about the relationship of structure to potency. It is evident that the three series of molecules in Table 2 obey different relationships to the ^1X index. Another observation is that with increasing ^1X value (increasing size) the potency increases; however, there is a maximum potency encountered when an optimum size is reached. This optimum value is different for each of the three series. Larger molecules become less potent following a regular decline in value with size.

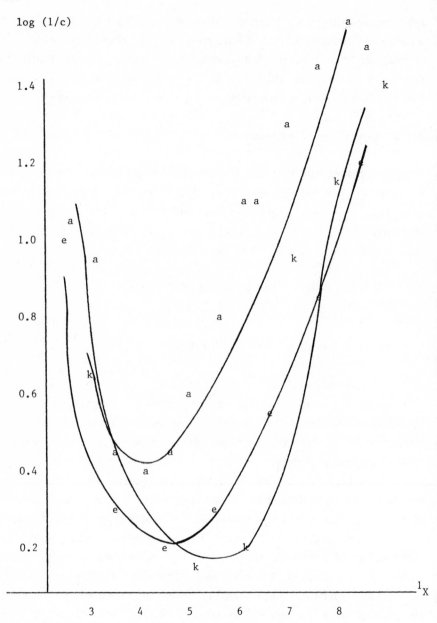

FIGURE 2.   log (l/c) vs ^{1}X for alkanes (a), ethers (e)
and ketones (k).

TABLE 2. AD_{100} values for loss of righting reflex of mice by aliphatic hydrocarbons, ethers, and ketones.

Compound	^1X	$^4X_p^v$	log (1/c) Obs.[a]	log (1/c) Calc.[b]
Pentane	2.414	0.354	1.052	1.167
Hexane	2.914	0.500	0.941	0.777
Heptane	3.414	0.677	0.458	0.614
Octane	3.914	0.854	0.391	0.552
Nonane	4.414	1.030	0.428	0.575
Decane	4.914	1.207	0.613	0.633
Undecane	5.414	1.384	0.810	0.743
Dodecane	5.914	1.561	1.124	0.869
Tridecane	6.414	1.737	1.119	1.020
Tetradecane	6.914	1.914	1.294	1.189
Pentadecane	7.414	2.091	1.516	1.367
Hexadecane	7.914	2.268	1.566	1.554
Heptadecane	8.414	2.444	1.538	1.755
Ethyl ether	2.414	0.204	1.036	0.944
Propyl ether	3.414	0.391	0.305	0.188
Butyl ether	4.414	0.595	0.104	-0.072
Pentyl ether	5.414	1.010	0.297	0.187
Hexyl ether	6.414	1.364	0.535	0.465
Heptyl ether	7.414	1.717	0.869	0.811
Octyl ether	8.414	2.071	1.188	1.201
3-Pentanone	2.808	0.250	0.657	0.517
4-Heptanone	3.808	0.683	0.121	0.366
5-Nonanone	4.808	0.873	-0.081	0.179
6-Undecanone	5.808	1.269	0.076	0.461
7-Tridecanone	6.808	1.623	0.978	0.774
8-Pentadecanone	7.808	1.976	1.127	1.136
9-Heptadecanone	8.808	2.330	1.455	1.543

[a]Drug dose in millimoles per kilogram.

[b]Calculated using eqn. (6).

Figure 2 reveals a parabolic relationship between log $(1/c)$ and ^1X. A quadratic equation, however, would not reflect the differences in optimum values among the three series nor would it capture very much of the difference encountered in the potencies of larger molecules beyond the optimum size. The presence of optimum values differing among the three series requires a second equation term. This second term must encode information about differing numbers of heteroatoms among the three series. This is the role of the $^4X_p^v$ index in the equation. By expressing ^1X as a reciprocal, the term encodes an increase in potency with size. However when the second term increases sufficiently in magnitude, it reflects a decrease in potency beyond an optimum size. Finally, the second term, as a valence index, is lower when more heteroatoms are present, reflecting greater potency from the presence of this feature. The three sets in the database are correctly ordered according to potency and the presence of an optimum value is encoded. This analysis shows a quadratic expression in ^1X would be inadequate as is born out in this case.

If we locate the log $(1/c)$ values on a ^1X vs $^4X_p^v$ graph, it can be shown that there is a region in ^1X, $^4X_p^v$ space where the most potent compounds are to be found. This is centered at $^1X = 4.5 \pm 0.3$, $^4X_p^v = 0.7 \pm 0.2$. From the equation we predict that among alkyl esters, butyl propionate or propyl butyrate might be among the most potent in this assay since both compounds have $^1X = 4.308$ and $^4X_p^v = 0.863$.

5.   QSAR of Muscarinic Antagonists

Kier and Hall (1978) have reported on the QSAR of a large number of muscarinic antagonists. The biological measurement was the muscarinic receptor affinity, log (k), for 104 compounds with the general formula $R_1-CH_2-CH_2-R_2$. The R_1 groups are listed in Table 3 and R_2 groups are listed in Table 4. The 104 compounds derived from a permutation of R_1 and R_2 in Tables 3 and 4 were analysed

TABLE 3. Connectivity indexes and log K contributions of bulky
fragment models.

Group Model	$^4X_{pc}$	Average	$^1X^v$	$^3X^v_c$	Average	Calc'd Log K Contrib.
$CH_3CH_2OC_2H_5$	0	0	1.992	0	0	1.341
$CH_3CH_2CH_2C_2H_5$	0	0	2.414	0	0	1.450
$C_6H_5CH_2COOC_2H_5$	0.777	0.155	4.022	0.177	0.089	2.684
$C_6H_5CH_2CH_2OC_2H_5$	0.433	0.144	4.040	0.118	0.118	2.354
$C_6H_5CH_2CH_2CH_2CH_2H_5$	0.433	0.144	4.471	0.118	0.118	2.463
$C_6H_{11}CH_2COOC_2H_5$	0.777	0.155	4.982	0.263	0.132	3.047
$C_6H_{11}CH_2CH_2OC_2H_5$	0.433	0.144	5.009	0.204	0.204	2.717
$C_6H_{11}CH_2CH_2CH_2C_2H_5$	0.433	0.144	5.432	0.204	0.204	2.826
$(C_6H_5)_2CHCOOC_2H_5$	1.799	0.106	6.091	0.313	0.078	4.165
$(C_6H_5)_2CHCH_2OC_2H_5$	1.381	0.106	6.091	0.295	0.098	3.828
$(C_6H_5)_2CHCH_2CH_2C_2H_5$	1.381	0.106	6.514	0.295	0.098	3.937
$(C_6H_5)_2C(OH)COOC_2H_5$	3.563	0.111	6.199	0.439	0.063	5.683
$(C_6H_{11})_2CHCOOC_2H_5$	1.799	0.106	7.992	0.478	0.120	4.877
$(C_6H_{11})_2CHCH_2OC_2H_5$	1.381	0.106	7.992	0.469	0.156	4.552

using molecular connectivity. The best three variable equation and
statistics reported are:

$$\log (K) = 0.749\,^4X_{pc} + 0.250\,^1X^v + 1.340\,^3X^v_c + 0.827 \qquad (7)$$
$$r = 0.962, \quad s = 0.331, \quad n = 104, \quad F = 417$$

TABLE 4.   Connectivity indexes and log (K) contributions of onium
group models

Group Model	$^4X_{pc}$	Average	$^1X^v$	$^3X^v_c$	Average	Calc'd Log K Contrib.
$C_2H_5N(CH_3)_3$	0.061	0.354	2.221	1.274	0.319	3.902
$C_2H_N(CH_3)_2(C_2H_5)_2$	1.707	0.285	2.808	0.986	0.247	4.151
$C_2H_5N(CH_3)(C_2H_5)_2$	2.030	0.226	3.396	0.757	0.189	4.238
$C_2H_5H(C_2H_5)_3$	2.121	0.177	3.983	0.577	0.144	4.216
$C_2H_5N(CH_2)_4CH_3$	1.634	0.182	3.481	0.757	0.189	3.963
$C_2H_5N(CH_2)_4C_2H_5$	1.811	0.151	4.069	0.577	0.144	4.006
$C_2H_5N(CH_2)_5CH_3$	1.634	0.182	3.981	0.757	0.189	4.092
$C_2H_5N(CH_2)_5C_2H_5$	1.811	0.151	4.569	0.577	0.144	4.135

A.   Random Number Analysis

When a regression equation is obtained from a search of several
variables, a question can be raised about possible random
correlations (Topliss and Costello, 1972). In this study this
question was addressed by an analysis of correlations based on the
replacement of the 22 chi terms with random numbers. A regression
analysis was used to find the best set of three variables influencing
the affinity data in the same manner as was done using chi indexes.
For each set of random numbers, 1540 triplets of variables were
considered. The highest correlation coefficient, r_{max}, was
recorded. The procedure was repeated 100 times with different sets
of random numbers for all 22 variables. The highest r_{max} value
found was 0.45 and the average was 0.25. Four values of r_{max}
were in the range 0.35-0.45, 35 were between 0.25 and 0.35, 60
were between 0.15 and 0.25, and one was below 0.15. In another

study, the three chi terms found to correlate with log (K), $^4X_{pc}$, $^1X^V$, and $^3X^V_c$, were regressed against 100 sets of random numbers in place of log (K). The highest correlation coefficient found was 0.35, and the average value was 0.16. Ten values lay in the range 0.25-0.35, 43 lay between 0.15 and 0.25, and 47 were between 0.05 and 0.15.

These studies clearly indicate that the set of three chi terms used in this study do not correlate with sets of random numbers, thus, the three chi terms in concert reflect the systematic variation of log (K) with the molecular structure. In addition, the chi terms yield a regression vastly superior to sets of random numbers. These results further support the conclusion that the correlation reported is a systematic relation.

B. Equation Analysis

The equation variables are no longer than three path lengths (three contiguous bonds as found in the $^4X_{pc}$ subgraphs). Indexes reflecting subgraphs through four path lengths were searched in the regression analysis. Additional regression analyses revealed no significant role for indexes based on paths of length five or six. This finding led to the conclusion that important structural features may be found at either end of the molecule but are not connected through the length of the molecule. Molecular connectivity provides a partial statement of the real structure of these molecules since the conformation is not dealt with by this method. The separate ends of the molecule, revealed by molecular connectivity to be important, may in fact be physically quite close because of forces influencing the conformational preference of the molecule. Molecular connectivity refers to sequential attachment of atoms through formal bonds, not transspatial nonbonded forces and interactions.

The finding of a separate role for the two ends of the molecule, in the sense just described, prompted an additional study to analyze separately the onium group and the side chain for further structural information.

C. Onium Group Fragment

For convenience in analyzing the eight onium group variants, a truncated model of the onium groups was adopted in which the remainder of the molecule was replaced in each case by an ethyl group. Table 4 lists the values of the three connectivity indexes and the average value of chi per subgraph. Analysis of the data illustrates a number of structure-activity relationship conclusions about the onium groups and affinity. The first four onium groups in Table 4 are a homologous series formed by successively replacing an N-methyl group with an ethyl group. The number of subgraphs composing the $^4X_{pc}$ index increased by three through this series; however, the numerical values of the subgraph contributions, as illustrated by the average value, decreased in this progression. The net effect was a modest increase in the value of $^4X_{pc}$ after the second compound.

The $^3X_c^v$ index reveals a different trend in Table 4 for the first four cases. The number of subgraph terms comprising this index in each case was four, while the average value declined. The $^3X_c^v$ indexes decreased with successive ethyl group replacement. The $^1X^v$ indexes increased through this series, reflecting the addition of one carbon atom in each case.

A summation of these three connectivity indexes, weighted by the coefficients in the regression equation, reveals a contribution to the log (K) values from the onium group. As can be seen in the last column of Table 4, this contribution was quite similar through the series. The numerical range through all eight cases was within the standard deviation of the equation. An analysis of all eight onium group models in Table 4 gives the same conclusion. The contributions to log (K) from increasing the number of atoms was offset by a decline in the ^3X_c terms and a leveling out of the values of the $^4X_{pc}$ terms. The net result was a relatively constant contribution to log (K) by the onium group, irrespective of the increase in size or complexity.

D. Bulky Group Fragment

The bulky fragment was treated similarly by analyzing the individual connectivity indexes for truncated models of the side chains found in this study. The truncation model utilized an ethyl group terminating the molecule in place of the ethylonium group found in each actual compound. The data for analysis are summarized in Table 3. The major variation of affinity with molecular structure was associated with bulky group variation. This influence was encoded in all three connectivity indexes. The major fraction of the variation was described by the $^1X^V$ contribution. The range of $^1X^V$ influence was about 2 log (K) units while the influence from $^3X_c^V$ and $^4X_{pc}$ ranged over 0.5 and 0.7 log (K) units, respectively.

A more specific analysis of the data can be made in terms of structural features contributing to affinity. The replacement of a methylene group by an ether oxygen decreased the value of $^1X^V$ by 0.422. This difference reflected the observations that the ether side chains had a slightly lower affinity than the alkyl side chains. Cyclohexyl substituents gave $^1X^V$ values 0.96 higher than phenyl substituents, mirroring the trend in affinities. The replacement of a methyl hydrogen in the hydrocarbon or ether series by a phenyl or cyclohexyl group increased the affinity significantly. This effect was described principally by the increase in $^1X^V$. However, when both groups appeared on the same carbon, additional $^4X_{pc}$ and $^3X_c^V$ subgraphs were generated, giving an increase in affinity greater than anticipated based on the individual contributions. This observation was properly accounted for by eqn. (7) and corresponds to an earlier report, (Barlow, et al, 1963) but here it was revealed in quantitative form.

E. Prediction of Antagonist Affinities

One value of the structural descriptions encoded in eqn. (7) lies in the ability to predict the affinities of antagonists not included in

TABLE 5. Prediction of antagonist affinities.

Molecule	$^4X_{pc}$	$^1X^v$	$^3X^v_c$	Experimental log (K)	Calc'd log (K)
$C_6H_5(CH_2)_4N(CH_3)_3$	1.183	5.278	1.392	4.771	4.949
$C_6H_5(CH_2)_6N(CH_3)_3$	1.183	6.278	1.392	5.393	5.198
$C_6H_5(CH_2)_4N(C_2H_5)_3$	2.399	7.040	0.695	5.480	5.371
$C_6H_5(CH_2)_6N(C_2H_5)_3$	2.399	8.040	0.695	5.970	5.629
$(C_6H_5)_2\overset{\lceil O \rceil}{C}OCHCH_2N(CH_3)_3$	3.541	7.584	1.744	8.020	7.773

the original regression analysis. Accordingly, the chi indexes were calculated for five additional antagonists and the log (K) values were computed from eqn. (7) (Table 5). The predicted values of the affinities were within the standard deviation of the equation.

F. Prediction of Agonist Affinities

As a further test of eqn. (7) and to determine whether comparable structural features may govern the affinities of agonists, eqn. (7) was used to predict the affinities of five agonists and three partial agonists. The results (Table 6) reveal good predictions in almost every case. The standard deviations found were within the standard deviation of the original equation.

G. General Comments

Based on a quantitative structure-activity relationship accounting for 93% of the variation in the log (K) values for 104 molecules, certain general conclusions about structure and affinity can be made.

TABLE 6.   Prediction of agonist affinities.

Molecule	$^4X_{pc}$	$^1X^v$	$^3X_c^v$	Exp log (K)	Calc log (K)
$C_2H_5OCH_2CH_2N(CH_3)_3$	0.750	3.298	1.274	4.074	3.947
$C_2H_5OCH_2CH_2N(CH_3)_2C_2H_5$	1.457	3.885	0.986	3.887	4.242
$C_2H_5OCH_2CH_2CH_2N(C_2H_5)_2CH_3$	1.832	4.473	0.757	3.735	4.368
$C_2H_5OCH_2CH_2N(CH_2)_4CH_3$	1.436	4.559	0.757	4.026	4.093
$C_2H_5OCH_2CH_2N(CH_2)_4C_2H_5$	1.665	5.146	0.577	3.883	4.167
$C_2H_5CH_2CH_2CH_2N(CH_3)_3$	0.750	3.721	1.274	3.733	4.056
$C_2H_5CH_2CH_2CH_2N(CH_3)_2C_2H_5$	1.457	4.308	0.986	3.970	4.351
$C_2H_5CH_2CH_2CH_2N(CH_2)_4CH_3$	1.436	4.981	0.757	4.165	4.202

The affinity of the antagonists in Table 3 depends on a specific combination of molecular size, branching, and heteroatom composition. The onium group contribution to the affinity of the molecule is essentially constant, despite structural changes such as size and cyclization (Table 4). The variation in the onium group contribution to log (K) ranges from 3.902 to 4.238 for the eight variations in this study. This range coincides with the standard deviation in the equation.

The same kind of analysis applied to the onium groups of the agonists in Table 6 also reveals a fairly constant contribution to the log (K) values. Furthermore, these onium group contributions are the same as those found among the antagonists. This finding is quite compatible with the views of Barlow et al. (1963). The principal influence on the affinity of antagonists arises from structural variation in the side chain. This finding is evident from Table 3, which depicts the contributions from 14 different side chains in the study. The close predictions for antagonists and agonists in Tables 5 and 6 indicate that the molecular connectivity indexes in the equation accurately describe the structural influences governing the affinity.

6. Hallucinogenic Potency

Kier and Hall (1977) have examined the QSAR of a series of ring substituted amphetamine molecules using molecular connectivity. A sizeable amount of data has been made available on the relative hallucinogenic potency, in humans, of ring substituted amphetamines and mescalines. From the substituted amphetamine data, the potency, $\log \mu$, can be equated to the contribution of three connectivity indexes:

$$\log \mu = 45.16/^3x_p + 1.288\,^6x_p - 4.298/^4x_{pc}^v - 5.592 \tag{8}$$

$$r = 0.920, \quad s = 0.251, \quad n = 23, \quad F = 35$$

The compounds with potency are listed in Table 7.

A. Chance Correlation with Random Numbers

A criticism could be raised that some set of three chi terms from study 6 may give significant correlation with random numbers. This was analysed by running a search program against 2600 sets of random numbers and printing out the best correlation found for sets of three chi terms. By this technique, 163,200 sets of three chi terms were correlated against random numbers. Only 4% of the r values for the best three-variable correlations lay in the range of 0.6 - 0.77 and 0.77 was the highest value found. This study clearly established that these chi terms are not producing random correlations at a significant level, especially compared to the correlation of the chi terms against the biological activity. In an additional analysis, the three chi variables were replaced by random numbers and the regression against the activity was carried out. This procedure was repeated 100 times. The average r value obtained was 0.353, with no r value exceeding 0.75.

B. Analysis of Equation Terms

The statistical analysis of the relationship revealed that there is unexplained by the equation 20% of the activity (in log μ). This compares well with the 25% variation in the activity estimated from this testing technique. Thus a correlation much above 0.9 may have a diminished significance in view of this uncertainty. Even so, the attainment of a correlation coefficient of 0.92 in this study marked a new high in relating structure with activity among such a large list of hallucinogenic amphetamines. The correlation is high enough and the list sufficiently broad so that there was an opportunity to draw some conclusions about the salient structural features contributing to the activity.

For this analysis each of the connectivity terms was considered separately for their encoded influence on activity due to change in structure. The greater the number of adjacent ring substituents, the greater the value of ^3X_p. Compare compound 4 with 7 in Table 7. This connectivity term is also increased (due to two extra subgraph terms) when a methylenedioxy group replaces a pair of methoxyl groups in the same position. The contribution to the calculated activity is a net reduction. Compare 14 with 8, 4 with 11, and 9 with 15. Ring substituents longer than two major atoms (as in a methoxyl group) result in an increased value of ^3X_p, hence a lower calculated activity. Compare 17 with 8 and 20 with 21-23. Longer ring substituents would concurrently increase the ^6X_p term but sixth-order subgraph values are small relative to ^3X_p subgraph values; hence the effect on activity is governed primarily by the ^3X_p index. Increasing the number of substituents tends to increase the ^3X_p term contributing to a lowering of the calculated log μ value. Compare 8 with 9 and 3 with 5. This effect is concurrent with an increase in the other two chi terms which tend to increase the

TABLE 7. Substituted amphetamines and predicted hallucinogenic activity.

No.	Ring position and group					^3X_p	^6X_p	$^4X^v_{pc}$	Exp[a] $\log \mu$	Calc[a] $\log \mu$
	2	3	4	5	6					
1			OCH_3			3.348	1.034	0.469	0.59	0.55
2	OCH_3		OCH_3			4.124	1.508	0.642	0.67	0.87
3	OCH_3		OCH_3			4.124	1.683	0.638	0.87	1.06
4		OCH_3	OCH_3	OCH_3		4.808	1.830	0.739	0.37	0.55
5	OCH_3	OCH_3		OCH_3		4.830	2.083	0.765	0.63	1.01
6	OCH_3		OCH_3		OCH_3	4.853	2.083	0.798	2.08	1.12
7	OCH_3	OCH_3			OCH_3	4.933	2.045	0.810	1.14	1.06
8	OCH_3		OCH_3	OCH_3		4.892	2.058	0.785	1.26	1.00
9	OCH_3	OCH_3	OCH_3	OCH_3		5.629	2.363	0.917	0.86	0.92
10		$-OCH_2O-$				4.203	1.705	0.576	0.41	0.21
11		OCH_3	$-OCH_2O-$			4.925	2.252	0.707	0.43	0.62
12	$-OCH_2O-$		OCH_3			5.043	2.272	0.756	0.48	0.80
13	OCH_3	$-OCH_2O-$				5.027	2.197	0.753	1.00	0.71
14	OCH_3		$-OCH_2O-$			4.993	2.317	0.751	1.08	0.71
15	OCH_3	OCH_3	$-OCH_2O-$			5.746	2.749	0.885	0.75	1.09
16	OCH_3	$-OCH_2O-$		OCH_3		5.761	2.906	0.887	1.13	1.29
17	OCH_3		OC_2H_5	OCH_3		5.027	2.285	0.768	1.22	0.93
18	OCH_3		Br	OCH_3		4.574	1.762	1.157	2.71	2.92
19	OCH_3		CH_3	OCH_3		4.574	1.762	0.888	1.87	1.85
20	OCH_3		C_2H_5	OCH_3		4.892	2.058	0.910	2.01	1.70
21	OCH_3		$n\text{-}C_3H_7$	OCH_3		5.027	2.285	0.880	1.94	1.60
22	OCH_3		$n\text{-}C_4H_9$	OCH_3		5.296	2.436	0.880	1.63	1.34
23	OCH_3		$n\text{-}C_5H_{11}$	OCH_3		5.546	2.548	0.880	1.09	1.09

[a]Molar basis, converted by multiplying by the ratio of molecular weights of amphetamine to mescaline.

calculated activity. The net effect of increasing the number of substituents appears to be a balance resulting in a general prediction of the activity being less sensitive to the number of substituents than to their type and placement. Compare 3, 5, and 9 for roughly comparable activities in spite of different numbers of substituents.

The effect of the ^6X_p term is comparatively modest based on the small coefficient for the term and the low numerical values calculated for ^6X_p relative to the third- and fourth-order chi terms. Analogues with substituents in the 2 and 6 ring positions, such as methoxyl groups, have an extra ^6X_p subgraph; hence they contribute to an increased value of $\log \mu$. Compare 5 and 4 and also 14 and 11. Pairs of ring substituents like methoxyl groups positioned para to each other contribute an extra subgraph term of this order; hence, the numerical value of ^6X_p is increased, elevating the calculated activity. Compare 3 with 2 and 5 with 4. More substituents and/or longer substituents have a modest effect of increasing ^6X_p although the same structural effects increase the ^3X_p term to a greater extent, offsetting the influence on the calculated activity.

The $^4X_{pc}^V$ term is increased by additional ring substituents, resulting in an increase in calculated $\log \mu$. The number of substituents influences all chi terms leading to a complex effect based more on type and position than number. The $^4X_{pc}^V$ term is increased considerably when a ring substituent has a δ^V value less than one. Thus compound 18 is very active, reflecting $\delta^V = 0.250$ for the bromine. Substituents longer than two major atoms have no more subgraph terms for $^4X_{pc}^V$ but one subgraph has a $\delta^V = 2$ rather than $\delta^V = 1$. As a consequence the $^4X_{pc}^V$ is lower, decreasing the calculated $\log \mu$. Compare 21 with 20, 23 with 22, and 17 with 8.

Equation (8) meets three tests in the study. First, it affords a good correlation with the potency, accounting for over 80% of the variation in the data. Second, it allows for a considerable amount of SAR interpretation, compatible with the evidence and in agreement with previous empirical observations. A third test of the significance of the equation is the ability to use it to predict the activity of molecules not used in its derivation. To reveal this, there were considered three sets of molecules: amphetamines with indefinite values of activity, a number of mescaline derivatives, and molecules outside of the phenylalkylamine class. These three sets are found in Table 8 along with the computed connectivity terms.

The amphetamines in Table 8, entries 24-28, are molecules with indefinite statements of potency. The computed values, from eqn. (8), are converted to mescaline units (μ) and expressed as a range, based on the standard deviation of the equation. The agreement must be considered to be reasonably good, especially if it is noted that three of these values (compounds 24-26) are at the low end of the activity range used in computing eqn. (8). The predictions of the activity of compounds 27 and 28 are very good.

The second set of molecules predicted in Table 8 are six mescaline derivatives. A consideration of these compounds represents a departure from the basic structures used in developing the equation. The mescalines are phenethylamines, lacking the α-methyl group of the amphetamines. The predictions are very good. Evidently the absence of the α-methyl group is a deterrent to activity as seen in the comparisons of these molecules with the correspondingly substituted amphetamines in Table 7. The connectivity descriptions of the mescalines, relative to the amphetamines, revealed lower values for each connectivity term. The reduction in the $^4\chi_{pc}^v$ term, however, is about 20%, thereby constituting the major influence on the calculated activity.

The third set of molecules in Table 8 represent an attempt to use the equation to predict activities of two molecules which are major departures in structure from the phenylalkylamines. The prediction of the activities of two tryptamines from the equation are remarkably close to the experimental value in mescaline units, in spite of the fact that no tryptamine derivatives were used in deriving the equation.

The connectivity analysis of amphetamine SAR considered ring methoxyl, methylenedioxy, and alkyl groups, their number, and

Table 8. Predictions of Hallucinogenic Potency.

No	2	3	4	5	6	^3X_p	^6X_p	$^4X^v_{pc}$	μ Exp.	μ Calc.
			Ring Position							
			Amphetamines							
24	OCH_3	OCH_3	OCH_3			4.91	1.78	0.79	2	2-7
25		OCH_3	OCH_3			4.10	1.41	0.61	2	1-4
26	OCH_3	$-OCH_2O-$				4.92	2.25	0.71	1	2-7
27	OC_2H_5		$-OCH_2O-$			5.13	2.45	0.73	7	3-8
28	OCH_3		OCH_3	OC_2H_5		5.03	2.30	0.77	7	5-15
			Mescalines							
29			OCH_3			3.24	0.97	0.37	1	0.01-0.02
30		OCH_3	OCH_3			3.99	1.31	0.57	0.2	0.6-2.0
31		OCH_3	OCH_3	OCH_3		4.70	1.70	0.64	1	0.3-0.8
32	OCH_3		OCH_3	OCH_3		4.78	1.89	0.68	1	0.2-0.7
33	OCH_3	$-OCH_2O-$				4.91	2.03	0.65	5	0.3-1.1
34		OCH_3		$-OCH_2O-$		4.82	2.12	0.60	1	0.2-0.6
			Tryptamines							
35	4-Hydroxy-N,N-dimethyltryptamine					5.00	2.09	0.92	32	23-75
36	6-Hydroxy-N,N-dimethyltryptamine					4.93	2.22	0.90	25	26-51

TABLE 9. Hydrazide monoamine oxidase inhibitors.

$$R_3 - \bigcirc^{R_2\ R_1} - O - \underset{R_5}{\overset{R_4}{C}} - CO - NH - NH - R_6$$

Compound	R_1	R_2	R_3	R_4	R_5	R_6	$E_{\frac{1}{2}}$	pI_{50}
1.	H	H	H	H	H	$CH(CH_3)_2$	-0.4310	5.42
2.	Cl	H	H	H	H	$CH(CH_3)_2$	-0.4425	5.60
3.	H	Cl	H	H	H	$CH(CH_3)_2$	-0.4368	5.40
4.	H	H	Cl	H	H	$CH(CH_3)_2$	-0.4433	5.96
5.	CH_3	H	H	H	H	$CH(CH_3)_2$	-0.4390	5.54
6.	H	CH_3	H	H	H	$CH(CH_3)_2$	-0.4333	5.05
7.	H	H	CH_3	H	H	$CH(CH_3)_2$	-0.4355	5.40
8.	OCH_3	H	H	H	H	$CH(CH_3)_2$	-0.4365	5.62
9.	H	OCH_3	H	H	H	$CH(CH_3)_2$	-0.4365	5.42
10..	H	H	OCH_3	H	H	$CH(CH_3)_2$	-0.4353	5.52
11.	H	H	H	H	CH_3	$CH(CH_3)_2$	-0.4125	5.00
12.	Cl	H	H	H	CH_3	$CH(CH_3)_2$	-0.4148	5.16
13.	H	Cl	H	H	CH_3	$CH(CH_3)_2$	-0.4118	4.96
14.	H	H	Cl	H	CH_3	$CH(CH_3)_2$	-0.4155	5.00
15.	H	H	H	CH_3	CH_3	$CH(CH_3)_2$	-0.4025	4.34
16.	H	H	Cl	CH_3	CH_3	$CH(CH_3)_2$	-0.4133	4.80
17.	H	CH_3	H	H	CH_3	$CH(CH_3)_2$	-0.4115	4.90
18.	H	H	H	H	H	C_2H_5	-0.4232	5.82
19.	H	H	Cl	H	H	C_2H_5	-0.4262	6.00
20.	H	H	H	H	H	$CH_2C_6H_5$	-0.4448	6.14
21.	H	H	H	H	H	$CH(CH_3)C_6H_5$	-0.4340	5.70
22.	H	H	CH_3	H	H	$CH(CH_3)C_6H_5$	-0.4340	6.05
23.	H	H	OCH_3	H	H	$CH(CH_3)C_6H_5$	-0.4368	6.00
24.	H	H	Cl	H	H	$CH_2C_6H_5$	-0.4560	6.39

position. The absence of these functional groups in compounds 35 and 36 suggests the possibility that a broader interpretation of the connectivity indexes is possible in terms of salient structural features contributing to potency. Unfortunately, there is a limit to the possibility of exploring this aspect due to the relative paucity of comparable test data and the inherent uncertainties in available data. It can be concluded, however, that the molecular connectivity method has transcended structural similarities found in narrow chemical classes.

7. QSAR of Monoamine Oxidase Inhibitors

Fulcrand et al. (1978) analyzed a series of monoamine oxidase inhibitors and found good correlations between pI_{50} values and electronic and steric parameters for 24 compounds. Electronic effects, reflected in polarographic half-wave potentials, and steric effects were the most important parameters examined in the correlations. It was concluded that the monoamine oxidase inhibitory activity of the series was due to the hydrazide group, which could form an unstable diazene with the monoamine oxidase flavine coenzyme before rearrangement to bind on the enzyme.

Molecular connectivity indexes were calculated for these monoamine oxidase inhibitors (Richard and Kier, 1980), Table 9. Linear regression analysis by computer search for the three variables that gave the best correlation with activity yielded:

$$pI_{50} = -5.2 - 29.E_{\frac{1}{2}} - 0.82\,^2X + 1.8\,^3X_p^v \qquad (9)$$
$$r = 0.941, \quad s = 0.201, \quad F = 52, \quad n = 24$$

where $E_{\frac{1}{2}}$ represents the half-wave potential. This equation clearly indicates that electronic effects contribute to the monoamine oxidase inhibitor activity of the hydrazides, in agreement with Fulcrand et al. The ^2X index gives weight to structural features of two-bond lengths in the molecules, whereas the $^3X_p^v$ index represents three-bond path lengths within the molecules and also emphasizes the importance of the heteroatoms in the substituents.

To gain further insight into structural influences on the interaction between the inhibitors and the active enzyme site, regression analyses were run on a subseries of molecules formed by the deletion of certain substituent groups. In particular, the nitrogen substituent, R_6, was held constant with the isopropyl group to determine if this substituent was governing the inhibitory potency. This subset of 17 molecules, (1-17) in the table, correlates with pI_{50}:

$$pI_{50} = -4.1 + 0.59 \, {}^{0}X^{v} - 0.94 \, {}^{2}X - 23.E_{\frac{1}{2}} \qquad (10)$$
$$r = 0.951, \quad s = 0.134, \quad F = 41, \quad n = 17$$

Again, $E_{\frac{1}{2}}$ and ${}^{2}X$ emerge as significant parameters, but when ${}^{3}X_{p}^{v}$ is replaced by ${}^{0}X^{v}$, however, this valence chi index retains an indication of a contribution of heteroatoms in the substituents to activity.

If the R_4 and R_5 substituents are limited to hydrogen while R_6 is kept as isopropyl, then only 10 molecules remain, (1-10), in the table and the correlation is:

$$pI_{50} = -34. - 94.E_{\frac{1}{2}} - 2.6 \, {}^{4}X_{pc}^{v} \qquad (11)$$
$$r = 0.923, \quad s = 0.100, \quad F = 20, \quad n = 10$$

Electronic effects again contribute to the relationship. The ${}^{4}X_{pc}^{v}$ index relates well to systems where ring substitutions have been made and indicates that monoamine oxidase inhibitor activity of the hydrazides is related to the ring in some fashion, perhaps indirectly through its effects on the neighboring ether linkage. A further argument can be made for this point if all substituents from R_1 through R_5 are restricted to hydrogen and R_6 is varied: compounds 1, 18, 20 and 21 in the table. There is no correlation of the electronic parameter with the monoamine oxidase inhibitor activity.

Although the R_6 substituents certainly must affect the hydrazide, these observations would clearly argue against the hydrazide moiety as the sole contributor to biological activity. It may be concluded that the monoamine oxidase inhibitor activity of these hydrazides depends on the nature of the ring substitution as well as on the half-wave reduction potential of the ring, its substituents, or the ether oxygen. This view is reinforced by the fact that when R_1, R_2 and R_3 are successively substituted with the same group (compounds 2, 3, 4; 5, 6, 7; 8, 9, 10 and 12, 13, 14), the R_1 and R_3 have higher pI_{50} and lower $E_{\frac{1}{2}}$ values than the corresponding meta substituted compounds, R_2.

8. Discriminant Analysis of Taste

Molecular connectivity indexes may encode sufficient structural information to allow for a discrimination of two biological properties associated with structurally similar molecules. A case in point is a study by Kier (1980) on a series of cyclohexylaldoximes. These molecules were reported to possess bitter and sweet tastes in varying ratios. Ten predominantly sweet tasting and ten predominantly bitter tasting molecules were selected from the original study by Acton and Stone (1976), Tables 10 and 11.

A. Structural Analyses and Discrimination Analysis

The structural descriptions of the molecules in Tables 10 and 11 were made using molecular connectivity. Discriminant analysis is an approach to differentiate between two or more classes of molecules. The procedure is a search for a linear combination of structural variables that describes a line, plane, or general surface that separates the classes of molecules in the optimum manner. The function separates the categories with as little overlap as possible, thus providing discrimination between the categories.

The analysis also produces the critical value, y^*, so that molecules with $y > y^*$ are assigned to one category and those with $y < y^*$ are assigned to the other category. The quality of the discriminant function may be assessed in three ways: comparison of the F value to tabulated values, determination of the percentage of molecules correctly classified, and prediction of the classification of molecules not included in the original study. The best linear discriminant function, using two molecular connectivity index variables, is:

$$y = 1.21\,^1X - 3.88\,^4X_p \tag{12}$$

and the critical value is:

$$y^* = -3.27 \tag{13}$$

When each y value is solved for the sweet (Table 10) and bitter (Table 11) molecules, values of $y > -3.27$ are assigned to the sweet category while values of $y < -3.27$ are assigned to the bitter category. Therefore, when $y - y^*$ is negative, the molecule is classified as bitter. The discriminant function correctly assigns nine of the 10 sweet-tasting molecules (Table 10) and eight of the 10 bitter-tasting molecules (Table 11). The average percentage of correct assignment is 85%.

B.   Discussion

The linear discriminant function is an equation featuring two molecular connectivity indexes, ^1X and ^4X_p. These indexes, weighted by the coefficients in the equation, describe two structural characteristics which influence whether a molecule is sweet or bitter. The ^1X index describes the size of the molecule in terms of the number of bonds. Within the equation, the ^1X index indicates that the more bonds there are, the larger the y value will be. When ^1X is large enough, and $y > y^*$ the molecule is classified as sweet. The influence of size as expressed by ^1X is countered by the information conveyed by ^4X_p. This index, as a negative term in the linear discriminant function, leads to lower y values when ^4X_p increases.

TABLE 10. Discriminant analysis of sweet-tasting aldoximes.

Compound	R-CH=N-OH R	Taste Potency Relative to Sucrose	Percent of Taste, Sweet/Bitter	^1X	^4X_p	y-y*
1	*(structure)*	370	60/25	5.736	2.552	0.32
2	*(structure)*	1150	50/10	5.364	2.337	0.70
3	*(structure)*	50	65/10	6.244	2.965	-0.67
4	*(structure)*	55	48/7	3.932	1.707	1.41
5	*(structure)*	55	40/16	4.432	1.884	1.33
6	*(structure)*	135	65/7	6.274	2.788	0.05
7	*(structure)*	200	70/3	4.432	1.884	1.33
8	*(structure)*	500	78/3	4.826	2.026	1.25
9	*(structure)*	225	90/2	5.864	2.625	0.18
10	*(structure)*	300	92/1	6.274	2.788	0.05

TABLE 11. Discriminant analysis of bitter-tasting aldoximes R–CH=N–OH

Compound	R	Taste Potency Relative to Sucrose	Percent Taste Sweet/Bitter	l_X	^4X_p	$y - y^*$
1	*(structure)*	4	6/70	7.098	3.489	−1.67
2	*(structure)*	11	4/93	7.158	3.384	−1.19
3	*(structure)*	30	5/73	6.598	2.930	−0.11
4	*(structure)*	1.5	0/50	4.432	1.884	1.33
5	*(structure)*	2	2/65	4.432	1.884	1.33
6	*(structure)*	50	0/70	7.658	3.797	−2.19
7	*(structure)*	28	2/52	6.274	2.853	−0.20
8	*(structure)*	140	0/75	5.864	2.743	−0.27
9	*(structure)*	92	0/67	6.274	2.853	−0.20
10	*(structure)*	320	0/50	5.398	3.240	−2.77

The value of ^4X_p is influenced by the size of the molecule as well as by the substituents.

The indexes in the linear discriminant function indicate that the value of y is greater than that of y* when the number of first-row atoms in the substituent of cyclohexylaldoxime is four or less. A quarternary tert-butyl group (i.e., Compound 9, Table 12) has a y - y* of virtually zero. Substituents with more than four first-row atoms, particularly if they are branched, give a y value less than y* (Table 11). The structural conclusions are that larger, more branched substituents on cyclohexylaldoximes increase the tendency for the molecule to be bitter. In contrast, smaller substituents, with four or fewer first-row atoms, influence sweet taste (Table 10).

Another observation that can be made about the influence of structure on taste, based on the linear discriminant function, is that the two chi indexes are not of the valence class. This finding means that unsaturation or heteroatoms in the 20 molecules are not critical to the structures that influence the sweet or bitter taste. This conclusion is correct to the extent that 85% of the molecules are assigned correctly.

For the three incorrectly assigned molecules (3 in Table 10, and 4 and 5 in Table 11), a molecular connectivity index of the valence type may be necessary for the correct assignment. The addition of a third molecular connectivity index in the discrimination analysis failed to improve the number of correctly assigned molecules in Tables 10 and 11. The three incorrectly assigned molecules in Tables 10 and 11 have the lowest taste potencies among their respective taste classes. This observation suggests that high taste potency is important in the accurate categorization of molecules as bitter or sweet tasting. A test of the linear discriminant function and the molecular connectivity indexes that describe structures is the ability of the function and the associated critical value, y*, to predict the taste categories of molecules not in the original study. For this test, nine additional molecules were selected from the study of Acton and Stone (1976), based on their taste potencies and sweet-bitter taste ratios that favored one or the other category.

Calculation of the ^1X and ^4X_p indexes for each molecule and computation of y - y* for the linear discriminant function formed the basis of the taste category predictions shown in Table 12. The first five molecules are reported to be sweet. The predictions for 1-3 and 5 are correct. The prediction for 4 is ambiguous since y = y*. Compounds 6-9 are classified as bitter tasting. The solution of y - y* predicts 6, 8, and 9 to be bitter. Compound 7 is predicted incorrectly. Thus, seven of the predictions were correct, one was incorrect, and one was ambiguous. Without no. 4, the correct prediction for seven of eight compounds gave an accuracy of 87%, the same quality of classification as obtained with the assignments in Tables 10 and 11 combined.

The results of the study are encouraging in that molecular connectivity indexes appear to encode sufficient information about the structure influencing the taste category of cyclohexylaldoximes so that the discriminant analysis can assign correctly 17 of 20 molecules to the sweet or bitter taste category. Furthermore, the analysis based on these indexes can predict the taste category of additional molecules with the same accuracy. The study shows one approach to the possible separation of bitter taste from candidate molecules of interest as noncaloric sweeteners.

9. QSAR of Heterocycle Toxicity

Schultz et. al (1982) have studied the structural influences in a series of nitrogen heterocycles which exhibited toxicity to a fresh-water ciliate. The toxicity, log BR is - log C where C is the inhibitory concentration in moles. The list of compounds studied is shown in Table 13. A good equation was found in which the standard deviation did not exceed the error inherent in the data.

$$\log BR = 0.911\,^1X^V - 2.969 \qquad (14)$$
$$r = 0.962, \quad s = 0.27, \quad n = 24$$

Table 12. Taste Prediction from Discriminant Analysis.   R–CH=N–OH

Compound	R	Taste Potency Rel. to Sucrose	% of Taste, Sweet/Bitter	^1X	^4X_p	y–y*
1		90	50/15	4.432	1.884	1.32
2		80	50/20	6.274	2.788	0.05
3		52	5322	5.864	2.625	0.18
4		24	39/9	5.364	2.519	0.00
5		40	55/5	3.308	0.697	4.568
6		10	0/36	5.236	2.528	–0.20
7		175	14/34	5.364	2.444	0.28
8		10	0/38	7.958	3.593	–1.04
9		8	4/18	6.037	2.725	–0.01

TABLE 13.   Molecular connectivity index and log biological responses

for 24 nitrogen heterocyclic compounds.

No.	Heterocycle	$^1\chi^v$	log BR (observed)	log BR (predicted)	Residual value
1	Pyridine	1.850	−1.19	−1.28	0.09
2	3-Methylpyridine	2.260	−1.02	−0.91	−0.11
3	2,6-Dimethylpyridine	2.691	−0.81	−0.52	−0.29
4	Pyrazine	1.699	−1.82	−1.42	−0.40
5	2-Methylpyrazine	2.120	−1.09	−1.04	−0.05
6	2,3-Dimethylpyrazine	2.547	−0.87	−0.65	−0.22
7	Quinoline	3.264	0.01	0.00	0.01
8	2-Methylquinoline	3.685	0.47	0.39	0.08
9	2,6-Dimethylquinoline	4.096	0.68	0.76	−0.08
10	Quinoxaline	3.124	−0.30	−0.12	−0.18
11	2-Methylquinoxaline	3.545	0.02	0.26	−0.24
12	2,3-Dimethylquinoxaline	3.972	0.25	0.19	0.06
13	Acridine	4.679	1.40	1.29	0.11
14	Phenazine	4.549	1.40	1.18	0.23
15	Pyrimidine	1.699	−1.75	−1.42	−0.33
16	Pyridazine	1.716	−1.41	−1.41	0.00
17	Phthalazine	3.121	−0.34	−0.13	−0.21
18	Quinazoline	3.114	−0.29	−0.13	−0.16
19	Pyrrole	1.577	−1.11	−1.53	0.42
20	Indole	2.988	0.21	−0.25	0.46
21	1,2-Dimethylindole	3.799	0.84	0.49	0.35
22	Carbazole	4.405	0.91	1.04	−0.13
23	Pyrazole	1.437	−1.71	−1.66	−0.05
24	Imidazole	1.427	−1.00	−1.67	0.67

Finding a close relationship between log BR and the $^1X^V$ index makes it possible to describe some of the influences molecular structure has on toxicity. This dependence of log BR on $^1X^V$ indicates that with increasing number of atoms, toxicity levels also increase: compare compounds 1, 7, and 13; 4, 10 and 14; 19, 20, and 22 in Table 13. Similarly, the $^1X^V$ index encodes the information that increase in the heteroatom content of a ring increases toxicity: compare compounds 1 and 4, 7 and 10, 19 and 23. An exception to the latter case is noted with the tricyclic compounds numbers 13 and 14 where neither $^1X^V$ nor log BR vary much with the substitution of a second nitrogen atom.

10. Antiviral QSAR Using Fragments

In Chapter 6, section 3, it was shown that the structure implications from a QSAR equation based on molecular connectivity can be developed by examining the skeletal fragments (subgraphs) which make up the chi indexes in the regression equation. A second example is given here to illustrate further this technique and to underscore the importance of interpretation directly in terms of molecular structure.

A. Data Set and Regression Analysis

A series of alkyl substituted benzimidazoles was studied by Tamm (1953) in an investigation of activity against the Lee strain of the influenza B virus. The molecule names and activities are given in Table 14.

In an analysis using molecular connectivity indexes Hall and Kier (1978) found good correlations with long path terms as follows:

$$pC = 1.40\ ^6X_p + 1.11 \tag{15}$$
$$r = 0.950, \quad s = 0.17, \quad F = 120, \quad n = 15$$

TABLE 14. Antiviral Activity for Substituted Benzimidazoles

	Compound	^6X_p	Obs	Calc[a]	Diff
1	Benzimidazole	0.937	2.14	2.20	-0.06
2	2-Methyl	1.111	2.51	2.44	0.07
3	5-Methyl	1.236	2.72	2.62	0.10
4	5,6-Dimethyl	1.452	2.72	2.92	-0.20
5	4,6-Dimethyl	1.468	2.82	2.94	-0.12
6	2,5-Dimethyl	1.438	2.89	2.90	-0.01
7	4,5-Dimethyl	1.394	2.96	2.84	0.12
8	2,5,6-Trimethyl	1.715	3.05	3.29	-0.24
9	2,4,5-Trimethyl	1.627	3.20	3.16	0.04
10	5,6-Diethyl	1.912	3.39	3.56	-0.17
11	2-Propyl-5-methyl	1.936	3.60	3.60	0.00
12	2,4,5,6,7-Pentamethyl	2.051	3.66	3.76	-0.10
13	2-Ethyl-5-methyl	1.757	3.74	3.35	0.39
14	2-Butyl-5-methyl	2.014	3.77	3.71	0.06
15	2-Isopropyl-5-methyl	1.979	3.77	3.66	0.11

[a]Based on Eqn. (15).

$$pC = 1.89 \ ^6X_p - 0.677 \ ^4X_p^v + 1.04 \qquad (16)$$
$$r = 0.966, \quad s = 0.14, \quad F = 87, \quad n = 15$$

These equations are of sufficient statistical quality to be used for prediction of activity on untested compounds.

B. Structure Analysis

In a property-activity relationship study, Hansch (1972) found only a modest correlation with the partition coefficient, $r = 0.903$. The alkyl values used in the study are proportional to the number of substituent carbon atoms. This analysis suggests that only the number of substituent atoms is important and that the substituent size, branching, and pattern of substitution are not important. However, the appearance of high order connectivity path terms, sixth and fourth order, and one valence term in eqns. (15) and (16) strongly indicates the importance of the alkyl chain length and the pattern of substitution, in contrast to the Hansch analysis.

To investigate further the question of substitution pattern, the constituent subgraphs were analyzed in a manner somewhat like that described for the phenylpropyl ether data set in Chapter 6, section 3. In this present case major attention was focused on the efficacy of substitution on the five-membered ring in comparison to the six-membered ring.

All of the subgraphs contributing to the ${}^6X_p$ index are subdivided in various ways. For example, some sixth-order path subgraphs are contained wholly in the benzimidazole nucleus. The sum of these subgraphs, given the symbol R_{56}, doesn't include any substituent atoms.

The symbol S_6R_6 stands for the sum of subgraph terms including a substituent on the six-membered ring (S_6) and extending only over the six-membered ring (R_6). Other subgraphs include a substituent on the six-membered ring but also extend over both the six- and five-membered rings-S_6R_{56}.

In similar fashion terms may be defined for the five-membered ring as S_5S_5 and S_5R_{56}. Finally, some sixth-order path subgraphs include substituents on both rings and also extend over parts of both rings-$S_6S_5R_{56}$. For sixth-order paths there are six subclassifications as shown in Table 15. The superscript 6 identifies subfragments derived from ${}^6X_p$. An analogous set of subgraph classifications may be obtained for the ${}^4X_p^v$ index.

Fourth-order paths are not long enough to span the distance between substitutents on both rings. All of these subclassifications may be obtained from the CFUNC computing system that produces the file of chi indexes.

The first observation to be made is that sixth-order subgraphs contained wholly in the benzimidazole nucleus, $^6R_{56}$, do not contribute much to the correlation: $r^2 = 0.25$. This result is expected since these terms do not vary greatly with substituent changes.

The two best single subgraph terms for correlation with the activity involve five-membered ring substitution: $r = 0.69$ for $^6S_5R_{56}$ and $r = 0.72$ for $^4S_5R_5$. These partial chi indexes, each containing contributions from only a few of the total number of subgraphs, account for about 50% of the variation. These results suggest the importance of substitution on the five-membered ring.

Only six pairs of these subgraph variables yield a correlation equal in quality to eqn. (15) which utilizes all of the subgraphs in ^6X_p: $r = 0.93$. Three of the six equations contain $^6S_5R_{56}$; the other three contain $^4S_5R_5$. It is clear that a partial subgraph term involving five-membered ring substitution is required for quality correlation. No combination of terms that excludes five-membered ring substitution yields a high quality correlation. The best of these two variable equations is based on $^6S_6R_{56}$ and $^6S_5R_{56}$, for which $r = 0.941$.

These observations indicate the importance of: (a) alkyl substitution on the 2-position (five-membered ring) and (b) the combination of substitution on both five- and six-membered rings. The compound with the largest value of $^6S_5R_{56}$, 0.6193, is compound 15, the compound of highest activity.

The subgraph analysis may be continued by examination of three-variable equations. There are 19 sets of three-variable equations with $r = 0.94$. Sixteen sets include $^6S_5R_{56}$, again underscoring the importance of substitution on the five-membered ring. The other equations contain either $^6S_5R_{56}$ or $^4S_5R_{56}$. Furthermore, of the seven equations with $r = 0.95$, all contain $^6S_5R_{56}$. Also prominent in

TABLE 15.   Symbols for fragment (subgraph) classifications used in benzimidazole study.

| Symbol | Fragment includes (all or part of) Substituent on | | | Ring part of fragment is in | | |
	6-membered ring	5-membered ring	both rings	6-membered ring	5-membered ring	both rings
1. S_6R_6	X			X		
2. S_6R_{56}	X					X
3. S_5R_5		X			X	
4. S_5R_{56}		X				X
5. $S_6S_5R_{56}$			X			X
6. R_{56}						X

these high quality correlations are $^6S_6R_6$ and $^6S_5R_{56}$. It is significant that the $^6S_6S_5R_{56}$ term does not play an important role in any of the regression equations. Its appearance would have suggested that substitution on the 4-and 7-positions is more efficacious than on the 5-and 6-positions. However, there seems to be no discrimination among the six-membered ring positions.

The key term $^6S_5R_{56}$, is enhanced by large alkyl groups on the 2-postion; branched groups produce greater activity. Compare Compound 15 (2-isopropyl) with Compound 11 (2-propyl). Also, Compound 15 (2-isopropyl) is as active as Compound 14 (2-butyl), four carbon atom-substituent unbranched compared to three, branched. Apparently, cyclopropyl, sec-butyl, and tert-butyl groups may enhance activity as substituents on the 2-position.

C. Conclusions

For the alkylbenzimidazole data set, subgraph analysis shows that substitution of branched (or cyclic) alkyl groups on the 2-position (five-membered ring) is important for high activity. There is no discrimination between the four positions on the six-membered ring; activity does not depend on pattern of substitution in positions 4,5,6,7.

By use of the partial subgraph terms structurally significant portions of the biologically active molecule may be identified in cases where the activity may be highly related to a specific structural feature. The significance of the molecular fragment or substructure may even be put into quantitative terms by using the regression equation for the partial subgraph terms. The method of substructure identification by partial subgraph analysis can now be applied to more complex chemical systems.

11. General Summary

We have shown in these QSAR examples that a good equation model may be obtained using molecular connectivity indexes. The examples also illustrate that the indexes in these equations can be interpreted in terms of structural fragments. These fragments are identified and quantified in terms of their contribution to the measured biological activity. The ultimate value is a rationale for drug design or directed synthesis of molecules with desired properties.

References

Acton, E. M. and Stone, H. (1976). Potential new artificial sweetener from study of structure-taste relationships. Science, 193, 584-586.

Barlow, R. B., Scott, K. A. and Stephenson, R. P. (1963). An attempt to study the effects of chemical structure on the affinity and efficacy of compounds related to acetylcholine. Br. J. Pharmacol. Chemother. 21, 509-522.

DiPaolo, T. (1978). Molecular connectivity in quantitative structure-activity relationship study of anesthetic and toxic activity of aliphatic hydrocarbons, ethers and ketones. J. Pharm. Sci. 67, 566-568.

Fulcrand, P., Berge, G., Noel, A., Chevallet, P., Castel, J. and Orzalesi, H. (1978). Hydrazides as monoamine oxidase inhibitors. Eur. J. Med. Chem. 13, 177-182.

Gardner, R. J. (1979). Correlation of flavor thresholds of compounds in with molecular connectivity. MBAA Techn. Quart. 16, 204-211.

Hall, L. H. and Kier, L. B. (1978). Molecular connectivity and substructure analysis. J. Pharm. Sci., 67, 1743-1747.

Hansch, C. (1972). in "Biological Correlations, the Hansch Approach", W. van Valkenburg, Ed., ACS Advances in Chemistry Series 114, American Chemical Society, Washington, D.C.

Kier, L. B. and Hall, L. H. (1977). Structure-activity studies on hallucinogenic amphetamines using molecular connectivity. J. Med. Chem. 12, 1631-1636.

Kier, L. B. and Hall, L. H. (1978). Molecular connectivity study of muscarinic receptor affinity of acetylcholine antagonists. J. Pharm. Sci. 67, 1408-1412.

Kier, L. B. (1980). Molecular structure influencing either a sweet or bitter taste among aldoximes. J. Pharm. Sci. 69, 416-419.

Koch, R. (1983). Molecular connectivity index for assessing ecotoxicological behavior of organic compounds. Tox. and Environ. Chem. 6, 87-96.

Richard, A. J. and Kier, L. B. (1980). Structure-activity analysis of hydrazide monoamine oxidase inhibitors using molecular connectivity. J. Pharm. Sci. 69, 124-126.

Schultz, T. W., Kier, L. B. and Hall, L. H. (1982). Structure-toxicity relationships of selected nitrogenous heterocycle compounds using molecular connectivity. Bull. Environm. Contam. Toxicol. 28, 373-378.

Tamm, I., Folkers, K., Shunk, C. H., Heyl, D. and Horofall, F. L. (1953). Inhibition of influenza virus multiplication by alkyl derivatives of benzimidazole. J. Exp. Med., 98, 245-255.

CHAPTER 8
Published Studies
using Molecular Connectivity

Since the initial development of molecular connectivity, many papers have been published on this subject. The method has been applied to a variety of both physicochemical properties and biological activities. Several statistical techniques have been applied to QSAR problems using the chi indexes as the structure descriptors. It may be useful to the QSAR investigator to have a bibliographic listing of journal references in which molecular connectivity is prominent. The following is a nearly complete listing through 1984.

The references are listed under three catagories:

I.   Development of Methodology and Intepretation of
     Molecular Connectivity

II. Application to Physicochemical Properties

III. Application to Biological Activity

There are a total of 158 references listed. A few references are listed under two headings where two topics are discussed in the paper. These papers are marked with an asterisk at the point of the second listing.

1. Methodology and Interpretation

1. Molecular Connectivity I: Relationship to Nonspecific Local
   Anesthesia. L. B. Kier, L. H. Hall, W. J. Murray and M.
   Randic. J. Pharm. Sci., 64, 1971 (1975)

2. On Characterization of Molecular Branching. M. Randic. J. Am.
   Chem. Soc., 97, 6609 (1975)

3. Comparison of Several Molecular Topological Indexes With
   Molecular Surface Area in Aqueous Solution Estimation. G. L.
   Amidon and S. T. Anik, J. Pharm. Sci., 65, 801 (1976)

4. Molecular Connectivity 6: Examination of the Parabolic
   Relationship Between Molecular Connectivity and Biological
   Activity. W. J. Murray, L. B. Kier and L. H. Hall, J. Med.
   Chem., 19, 573 (1976)

5. Molecular Connectivity VII: Specific Treatment of Heteroatoms.
   L. B. Kier and L. H. Hall, J. Pharm. Sci., 65, 1806 (1976)

6. The Nature of Structure-Activity Relationships and their Relation
   to Molecular Connectivity. L. B. Kier and L. H. Hall, Eur. J.
   Med. Chem., 12, 307 (1977)

7. A Comparative Analysis of Molecular Connectivity, Hansch,
   Free-Wilson and Darc-pelco Methods in the SAR of Halogenated
   Phenols. L. H. Hall and L. B. Kier, Eur. J. Med. Chem., 13,
   89 (1978)

8. Molecular Connectivity and Substructure Analysis. L. H. Hall and
   L. B. Kier, J. Pharm. Sci., 67, 1743 (1978)

9. Comparison of Molecular Connectivity and Darc/Pelco Methods: Performance in Antimicrobial, Halogenated Phenol QSARS. C. Mercier and J. E. Dubois, Eur. J. Med. Chem., 14, 415 (1979)

10. Note on the Randic Molecular Connectivity Index. K. Altenburg, Z. Phys. Chemie. (Leipzig), 261, 389 (1980)

11. Structural Information from Molecular Connectivity XPC4 Index. L. B. Kier, J. Pharm. Sci., 69, 1034 (1980)

12. Method for Generating a Chemical Reaction Index for Storage and Retrieval of Information. M. A. Mosby and L. B. Kier, J. Chem. Inf. Comput. Sci., 20, 217, (1980)

13. Application of Verloop Parameters. Comparison with Other Steric Parameters and Problems of Choice of Parameters. G. Taillandier, M. Domard, and A. Boucherle, Farmaco Ed. Sci., 35, 89 (1980)

14. Derivation and Significance of Valence Molecular Connectivity. L. B. Kier and L. H. Hall, J. Pharm. Sci., 70, 583 (1981)

15. Connectivity in Chemical Graphs. M. Razinger, Theor. Chim. Acta., 61, 581 (1982)

16. Structural Information and a Flexibility Index from the Molecular Connectivity Path-3 Index. L. B. Kier and L. H. Hall, Quant. Struct.-Act. Rel., 2, 55 (1983)

17. General Definition of Valence Delta-Values for Molecular Connectivity. L. B. Kier and L. H. Hall, J. Pharm. Sci., 72, 1170 (1983)

2. Application to Physicochemical Properties

A. General Papers

1. Molecular Connectivity II: Relationship to Water Solubility and Boiling Point. L. H. Hall. L. B. Kier, and W. J. Murray, J. Pharm. Sci., 64, 1974 (1975)

2. Molecular Connectivity V: Connectivity Series Concept Applied to Density. L. B. Kier, W. J. Murray, M. Randic and L. H. Hall, J. Pharm. Sci., 65, 1226 (1976)

3. A Molecular Connectivity Study of Electron Density in Alkanes. L. H. Hall and L. B. Kier, Tetrahedron, 33, 1953 (1977)

4. The Relationship of pi-Binding Energy with Molecular Connectivity in Hydrocarbons. S. P. Gupta and P. Singh, Bull. Chem. Soc. Jpn,. 52, 2745 (1979)

5. Molecular Connectivity and Its Correlation With Physicochemical Properties 1: Boiling Points of Saturated Aliphatic Carboxylic Acids. V. K. Gombar, Pharmacos, 25, 46 (1981)

6. Quantitation of Solvent Polarity Based on Molecular Structure. L. B. Kier, J. Pharm. Sci., 70, 930 (1981)

7. The Relation of Physical Properties of Alkanes to Connectivity Indexes-A Molecular Explanation. J. T. Edward, Can. J. Chem., 60, 480 (1982)

8. Estimation of Substituent Group Electronic Influence from Molecular Connectivity Delta Values. L. B. Kier and L. H. Hall, Quant. Struct.-Act., 2, 163 (1983)

9. Novel Substituent Entropy Constant - Sigma SO -Represents the Molecular Connectivity-X and its Related Indexes. Y. Sasaki, T. Takagi, S. H. Kawaki and A. Iwata, Chem. Pharm. Bull., 31, 330 (1983)

10. Molecular Connectivity Parameter and Enthalpy of Mixing. D. D. Deshpande and P. Aravindakshan, Mat. Chem. Phys., 8, 171 (1983)

11. Correlation of Activity Coefficients of Hydrocarbons in Water at Infinite Dilution with Molecular Parameters. M. Medir and F. Giralt, AIChE J., 28, 341 (1983)

12. Criterion of Connectivity for Problems of Mathematical Synthesis of Molecular Structures using a Computer. B. B. Smirnov, T. S. Pivina and V. A. Shlyapochinikov, Izv. Akad. Nauk. SSSR, Ser. Kim., 10, 2396 (1984)

13. Hierarchically Ordered Extended Connectivities. NMR Chemical Shifts of Condensed Benzenoid Hydrocarbons. O. Mekenyan, D. Bonchev and A. T. Balaban, Chem. Phys. Lett., 109, 85 (1984)

14. Spirans. Relationships Between Mass Spectra Fragmentation Pathways and Molecular Connectivity Indexes in Some Oxa- and Thiaspirans. M. J. Mokrosz, B. Rys., J. L. Mokrosz and M. H. Paluchowska, Chem. Scr., 23, 240 (1984)

15. Correlations Between Topological Features and Physical Chemical Properties of Molecules. D. V. S. Jain, S. Singh and V. Gombar, Proc. Indian Acad. Sci., Chem. Sci., 93, 927 (1984)

16. Calculation of Heat of Formation: Molecular Connectivity and IOC-Omega Technique, a Comparative Study. V. K. Singh, V. P. Tewari, D. K. Gupta and A. K. Srivantava, Tetrahedron, 40, 2859 1984)

B. Chromatography

1. Hydrophobic Effects in Reversed Phase Liquid Chromatography.
    B. L. Karger, J. R. Grant, A. Hartkopf and P. H. Weiner, J.
    Chromatogr., 128, 65 (1976)

2. Molecular Connectivity and Retention Indexes. Y. Michotte and
    D. L. Massart, J. Pharm. Sci., 66, 1630 (1977)

3. The Relationship Between the Rm Values and the Connectivity
    Indices for Pyrazine Carbothioamide Derivatives. R. Kaliszan and
    H. Foks, Chromatogr. 10, 346 (1977)

4. Correlation Between the Retention Indexes and the Connectivity
    Indexes of Alcohols and Methyl Esters with Complex Cyclic
    Structure. R. Kaliszan, Chromatogr. 10, 520 (1977)

5. Correlation of Gas Chromatographic Retention Parameters with
    Molecular Connectivity. J. S. Millership and A. D. Woolfson, J.
    Pharm. and Pharmacol., 29, 75 (1977)

6. The Relation Between Molecular Connectivity and Gas
    Chromatographic Retention Data. J. S. Millership and A. D.
    Woolfson, J. Pharm. and Pharmacol., 30 483 (1978)

7. A Relationship between the Connectivity Indices and Retention
    Indices of Polycyclic Aromatic Hydrocarbons. R. Kaliszan and J.
    Lamparczyk, J. Chromomatgr. Sci., 16, 246 (1978)

8. Correlation Between Chromatographic Parameters and Connectivity
    Index in Liquid-Solid Chromatography. W. Markowski, T. Dzido
    and T. Wawizynowicz, Polish J. Chem., 52, 2063 (1978)

9. Molecular Connectivity Analysis of Structure Influencing Chromatographic Retention Indexes. L. B. Kier and L. H. Hall, J. Pharm. Sci., 68, 120 (1979)

10. Connectivity Parameters as Predictors of Retention in Gas Chromatography. T. R. McGregor, J. Chrom. Sci., 17, 314 (1979)

11. Molecular Connectivity and Gas Chromatographic Retention Parameters. J. S. Millership and A. D. Woolfson, J. Pharm. Pharmacol., 32, 610 (1980)

12. Selectivity of Homogeneous Series in Reversed Phase Liquid Chromatography I: Theory. H. Colin and G. Gwochon, J. Chrom. Sci., 18, 54 (1980)

13. An Analysis of Molecular Connectivity: Chromatographic Retention Indexes in Alcohols, Ketones, Ethers, and Esters. R. Carbo and A. J. Farre, Afinidad, 37, 491 (1980)

14. Prediction of Gas Chromatographic Retention Indices from Linear Free Energy and Topographic Parameters. L. Buydens and D. L. Massart, Anal. Chem., 53, 1990 (1981)

15. Correlation of Reversed-Phase Capacity Factors for Barbiturates with Biological Activities, Partition Coefficients, and Molecular Connectivity Indexes. M. J. M. Wells, R. C. Clark and R. M. Patterson, J. Chromatogr. Sci., 19, 573 (1081)

16. Investigation of N-Alkylbenzamides by Reversed-Phase Liquid Chromatography III: Correlation of Chromatographic Parameters with Molecular Connectivity Indices for the C1-C5 N-alkylbenzamides. M. J. M. Wells, R. C. Clark and R. M. Patterson, J. Chromatogr., 235, 61 (1982)

17. Investigation of N-Alkylbenzamides by Reversed-Phase Liquid Chromatography V. Characteristics of Some Alkylbenzamides. M. J. M. Wells and R. C. Clark, J. Chromatogr., 244, 231 (1982)

18. Comparison of Molecular Connectivity and a Chromatographic Correlation Factor in Reversed-Phase High-Performance Liquid Chromatography for Polycyclic Aromatic Hycrocarbons. R. J. Hurtubise, T. W. Allen and H. F. Silver, J. Chromatogr., 235, 517 (1982)

19. Relationship between Connectivity Indexes of Pyrido(1,2a)pyrimid-in-4-ones and their Liquid-Liquid Partition Data Obtained by Gas-Liquid Chromatograaphy. G. Szasz, K. Valko, O. Papp and I. Hermecz, J. Chromatogr., 243, 347 (1982)

20. Investigation of N-Alkylbenzamides by Reversed-Phase Liquid Chromatography. IV: The Study of a Homologous Series of N-Alkylbenzamides Using the Solvophobic Theory and Molecular Connectivity. M. J. M. Wells and R. C. Clark, J. Chromatogr., 243, 263 (1982)

21. Relationship Between Molecular Connectivity Indexes of Barbiturates and Chromatographic Parameters. J. Bojarski and L. Ekiert, Chromatographic, 15, 172 (1982)

22. Analysis of Complex Mixtures of Aromatic Hydrocarbons. Relations Between Retention Index and Molecular Structure. J. Bermejo, J. S. Canga and O. M. Gayol, Int. J. Environ. Anal. Chem., 11, 271 (1982)

23. Retention Index, Connectivity Index and van der Waals Volume of Alkanes. F. Sauro Calixto and A. Garca Raso, Chromatogr., 15, 521 (1982)

24. Evaluation of Modified Valence Molecular Connectivity Index for Correlations of Chromatographic Parameters. J. Bojarski and L. Ekiert, J. Liq. Chrom., 6, 73 (1983)

25. Comparative Study of Topological and Linear Free Energy-related Parameters for the Prediction of GC Retention Indices. L. Buydens, D. Coomans, M. Vanbelle, D. L. Massart, and R. Vanden Driessche, J. Pharm. Sci., 72, 1327 (1983)

26. Correlations Between Retention Data of Isomeric Alkylbenzenes and Physical Parameters in Reversed-phase Micro High-performance Liquid Chromatography. K. Jinno and K. Kawasaki, Chromatogr., 17, 337 (1983)

27. Relation Between Retention Indexes of Homologous Compounds and the Number of Carbon Atoms and Polarity of the Stationary Phase (GLC). Equivalence Between Different Molecular Parameters. F. Sauro Calixto, R. Garcia and J. Canellas, An. Quim., Ser. C, 79-(3)suppl 1, 411 (1983)

28. Reversed-Phase Liquid Chromatographic Elution Characteristics of Substituted N-Ethylbenzamides. P. Lehtonen, J. Chromatogr., 267, 277 (1983)

29. Relationships Between Molecular Connectivity Indexes, Partition Coefficients and Chromatographic Parameters. G. Szasz, O. Papp, J. Vamos, K. Hanko-Novak and L. B. Kier, J. Chromatogr., 269, 91 (1983)

30. Experimental Evaluation of Relative Partition Coefficients by Gas Chromatography. D. Rehn, W. Zerling and U. Pust, Pharm. Acta. Helv., 58, 144 (1984)

31. Relation Between Gas Chromatographic Retention Indices and Molecular Connectivities of Nitrated Polycyclic Aromatic Hydrocarbons. P. J. Doherty, R. M. Hoes and A. Robbat, Anal. Chem., 56, 2697 (1984)

32. Correlation Between the Retention Data of Polycyclic Aromatic Hydrocarbons and Several Descriptors in Reversed-phase HPLC. K. Jinno and K. Kawasaki, Chromatogr., 17, 445 (1984)

33. Retention Prediction of Substituted Benzenes in Reversed-phase HPLC. K. Jinno and K. Kawasaki, Chromatogr., 18, 90 (1984)

34. Selectivity of a Phenyl-bonded Silica Gel. T. Hannai and J. Hubert, J. Chromatogr., 291, 81 (1984)

35. Calculation of Retention Indexes by Molecular Topology: Chlorinated Alkanes. A. Sabljic, J. Chromatogr., 314, 1 (1984)

36. Relation Between Gas Chromatographic Retention Indexes and Connectivity Parameters for Polycyclic Aromatic Hydrocarbons. B. A. Rudenko, Z. Y. Bulycheva and L. V. Dylevskaya, Zh. Anal. Khim., 39, 344 (1984)

37. High-Performance Liquid Chromatography of Alkylbenzenes. Relationship with Lipophilicities as Determined from Octanol-water Partition Coefficients or Calculated from Hydrophobic Fragmental Data and Connectivity Indexes; Lipophilicity Predictions for Polyaromatics. R. E. Koopmans and R. F. Rekker., J. Chromatogr., 285, 267 (1984)

38. The Evaluation of Molecular Connectivity Indexes and van der Waals Volumes for Correlation of Chromatographic Parameters. J. Bojarski and L. Ekiert, Anal. Chem. Symp. Ser.. Vol. 16, New Approaches Liq. Chromatogr., pp 35-41, (1984)

39. Chemical Structure and Liquid Chromatographic Behavior Among
    Nitrogen-bridged Compounds. A. Shalaby, Z. Budvari-Barany, K.
    Hanko-Novak, G. Szasz and I. Hermecz, Anal. Chem. Symp. Ser.,
    Vol. 16, New Approaches Liq. Chromatogr., pp 165-188 (1984)

C. Partition Coefficient and Solubility

1. *Molecular Connectivity II: Relationship to Water Solubility and
    Boiling Point. L. H. Hall, L. B. Kier, and W. J. Murray,
    J. Pharm. Sci., 64, 1974 (1975)

2. Molecular Connectivity III: Relationship to Partition
    Coefficients. W. J. Murray, L. H. Hall and L. B. Kier, J. Pharm.
    Sci., 64, 1978 (1975)

3. Correlation of Log P with Molecular Connectivity in Hydroxyureas:
    Influence of Conformational System on Log P. G. R. Parker,
    J. Pharm. Sci., 67I, 513 (1978)

4. Molecular Topology and Aqueous Solubility of Aliphatic Alcohols.
    A. Cammarata, J. Pharm. Sci., 68, 839 (1979)

5. Solubility Prediction Under the Screening Conditions of
    Biologically Active Compounds. Part 2. Additive and Semiempirical
    Approaches. N. A. Epshtein, and S. V. Nizhnii, Pharm. Chem.
    J. (USSR), 13, 392 (1980)

6. *Correlation of Reversed-Phase Capacity Factors for Barbiturates
    with Biological Activities, Partition Coefficients, and Molecular
    Connectivity Indexes. M. J. M. Wells, R. C. Clark and R. M.
    Patterson, J. Chromatogr. Sci., 19, 573 (1981)

7. The Relationship Between Molecular Connectivity and Partition
    Coefficients. J. C. Boyd, J. S. Millership and A. D. Woolfson,
    J. Pharm. Pharmacol., 34, 364 (1982)

8. Correlation of Alkane Solubilities in Water with Connectivity
    Index. J. T. Edward, Can. J. Chem., 60, 2573 (1982)

9. *High-Performance Liquid Chromatography of Alkylbenzenes.
    Relationship with Lipophilicities as Determined from
    Octanol-water Partition Coefficients or Calculated from
    Hydrophobic Fragmental Data and Connectivity Indexes;
    Lipophilicity Predictions for Polyaromatics. R. E. Koopmans and
    R. F. Rekker., J. Chromatogr., 285, 267 (1984)

3. Application to Biological Activity

A. General Applications

1. Molecular Connectivity 4: Relationship to Biological Activities.
    L. B. Kier, W. J. Murray, and L. H. Hall, J. Med. Chem., 18,
    1272 (1975)

2. Structure-Activity Studies Using Valence Molecular Connectivity.
    L. H. Hall and L. B. Kier, J. Pharm. Sci., 66, 642 (1977)

3. Molecular Connectivity and Steric Parameters. W. J. Murray, J.
    Pharm. Sci., 66, 1352 (1977)

4. Scope of Molecular Connectivity Index in Structure-Activity
    Relationship Studies. S. P. Gupta and P. Singh, Indian J. Chem.
    Sect. B, 16B, 709 (1978)

5. Quantitative Structure-Activity Relationships (QSAR) Studies of
    Pharmacological Agents Using Topological Information Content.
    C. Raychaudhury, S. C. Basak, A. B. Roy and J. J. Ghosh,
    Indian Drugs, 18, 97 (1980)

6. Quantitative Structure-Activity Relationships Studies of Bioactive
    Molecules Using Structural Information Indices. S. K. Ray, S.
    C. Basak, C. Raychaudhury, A. B. Roy and J. J. Ghosh,
    Indian J. Chem., 20B, 894 (1981)

7. The Relation of Molecular Connectivity to Molecular Volume and
    Biological Activity. L. H. Hall and L. B. Kier, Eur. J. Med.
    Chem., 16, 399 (1981)

8. A Quantitative Structure-Activity Relationships Study of N-Alkyl-
    norketobemidones and Triazinones Using Structural Information
    Content. S. K. Ray, S. C. Basak, C. Raychaudhury, A. B.
    Roy and J. J. Ghosh, Arzneim.-Forsch, 32, 322 (1982)

9. Application of Topological Molecular Transforms to Rational Drug
    Design. Z. Gabanyi, P. Surjan and G. Naray-Szabo, Eur. J.
    Med. Chem., 17, 307 (1982)

10. Structure-Activity Relationships and Pharmacokinetics: A
    Comparative Study of Hydrophobicity, van der Waals Volume and
    Topological Parameters. S. C. Basak, D. P. Gieschen, V. R.
    Magnuson and D. K. Hariss, IRCS Med. Sci. 10, 619 (1982)

11. Structure Activity Relationships using Molecular Connectivity
    Indexes with Principal Component Analysis. L. P. Burkhard,
    A. W. Andren, and D. E. Armstrong, Chemosphere, 12 935
    (1983)

12. Recent Advances in Molecular Connectivity for Biological SAR
    Analysis. L. B. Kier and L. H. Hall, IUPAC Pesticide Chemistry,
    Human Welfare and and the Environment, ed. J. Miyamoto,
    Pergamon Press, 351 (1983)

238

13. Surface Activity and Human Blood Platelet Aggregation Inhibitory Potency. R. P. Quintana, A. Lasslo and G. S. Queen, Chem. Biol. Interactions, 38, 135 (1983)

14. On the Use of Connectivity Indexes in Quantitative Structure-Activity Studies. R. Compadre, C. M. Compadre, R. Catillo and W. J. Dunn, III, Eur. J. Med. Chem., 18, 569 (1983)

15. Quantitative Structure-activity Considerations on the Spore-inhibiting Activity of Esters of 1,3-Dihydroxybutane. D. Rehn, Meth. Find. Exptl. Clin. Pharmacol., 5 701 (1984)

B. Anesthetics

1. Molecular Connectivity and Structure-Activity Relationship of General Anesthetics. T. Dipaolo, L. B. Kier and L. H. Hall, Molec. Pharmacol., 13, 31 (1977)

2. Structure-Activity Relationships of Anesthetic Ethers Using Molecular Connectivity. T. DiPaolo, J. Pharm. Sci., 67, 546 (1978)

3. Molecular Connectivity in Quantitative Structure-Activity Relationship Study of Anesthetic and Toxic Activity of Aliphatic Hydrocarbons, Ethers and Ketones. T. DiPaolo, J. Pharm. Sci., 67, 566 (1978)

4. Molecular Connectivity Study of Halocarbon Anesthetics. T. D. DiPaolo, L. B. Kier and L. H. Hall, J. Pharm. Sci., 68, 39 (1979)

5. Quantitative Correlation of Anesthetic Potencies of Halogenated Hydrocarbons with Boiling Point and Molecular Connectivity. M. C. Bindal, P. Singh and S. P. Gupta, Arzneim.-Forsch, 30, 234 (1980)

C. Flavor, Odor and Taste

1. Structure-Activity Studies on Odor Molecules Using Molecular Connectivity. L. B. Kier, T. DiPaolo and L. H. Hall, J. Theor. Biol., 67, 585 (1977)

2. Application of Property-Activity Relationships and Structure-Activity Relationships to Flavor Research, Part III: Correlation of Flavor Thresholds of Compounds in Beer with Molecular Connectivity. R. J. Gardner, Tech. Q.-Master Brew. Assoc. Am., 16, 204 (1979)

3. Application of Property-Activity Relationships and SAR to Flavor Research. R. T. Gardner, MBAA Tech. Quart., 16, 204 (1979)

4. Stereochemical Theory of Olfaction. A Quantitative Study. I. Motoc, F. Kerek, J. Riplos, M. Paunet and Z. Simon, Can. J. Pharm. Sci., 14, 96 (1979)

5. Molecular Structure Influencing Either a Sweet or Bitter Taste Among Aldoximes. L. B. Kier, J. Pharm. Sci., 69, 416 (1980)

6. Correlation of Bitterness Thresholds of Amino Acids and Peptides with Molecular Connectivity. R. J. Gardner, J. Sci. Food Agric., 31, 23 (1980)

7. Structure-Activity Studies on Sulfamate Sweeteners. 3. Structure-Taste Relationships for Heterosulfamates. W. J. Spillane, G. McGlinchey, I. O. Muircheartaigh and G. A. Benson, J. Pharm. Sci., 72, 934 (1983)

D. Psychomimetic and Hallucinogenic Activity

1. Structure-Activity Studies on Hallucinogenic Amphetamines using Molecular Connectivity. L. B. Kier and L. H. Hall, J. Med. Chem., 20, 1631 (1977)

2. Psychotomimetic Phenalkylamines as Serotonin Antagonists: An SAR Analysis. L. B. Kier and R. A. Glennon, Life Sci, 22, 1589 (1978)

3. LSD Analogs as Serotonin Antagonists: A Molecular Connectivity SAR Analysis. R. A. Glennon and L. B. Kier, Eur. J. Med. Chem., 13, 219 (1978)

4. Molecular Connectivity Analysis of Hallucinogenic Mescaline Analogs. R. A. Glennon, L. B. Kier and A. T. Shulgin, J. Pharm. Sci., 68, 906 (1979)

5. Quantitative Structure-Activity Studies on Hallucinogenic Mescaline Analogs using Modified 1st Order Valence Connectivity. S. P. Gupta, M. C. Bindal and P. Singh, Arzn-Forsch., 32, 1223, (1982)

6. Structure-activity Relationships in Opioid Peptides. D. Maysinger, M. Movrin, and M. Ljubic, Acta Pharm. Jugosl., 32, 177, (1982)

E. Toxicological and Environmental Applications

1. Molecular Connectivity: A Novel Method for Prediction of Bioconcentration Factor of Hazardous Chemicals. A. Sabljic and M. Protic, Chem.-Biol. Interactions, 42, 201 (1982)

2. Molecular Connectivity and Acute Toxicity of Environmental Pollutants. R. Koch, Chemosphere. 11, 925 (1982)

3. Relationship Between Molecular Connectivity Indices and Soil Sorption Coefficients of Polycyclic Aromatic Hydrocarbons. A. Sabljic and M. Protic, Bull. Environ. Contam. Toxicol., 28, 162 (1982)

4. Structure-Toxicity Relationships of Selected Nitrogenous Heterocyclic Compounds III: Relations Using Molecular Connectivity. W. Schultz, L. B. Kier and L. H. Hall, Bull. Environ. Contam. Toxicol., 28, 373 (1982)

5. Molecular Connectivity Index for Assessing Ecotoxicological Behavior of Organic Compounds. R. Koch, Tox. Environ. Chem., 6, 87 (1983)

6. Quantitative Structure-Toxicity Relationship of Chlorinated Compounds - A Molecular Connectivity Investigation. A. Sabljic, Bull. Environ. Contam. Tox., 30, 80 (1983)

7. Molecular Connectivity Indexes as Structure Chemical-Parameters of Substances with Ecotoxicological Relevance. R. Koch, Acta Hydochimica et Hydrobiologica, VII, 511 (1983)

8. Molecular Connectivity of Phenols and their Toxicity to Fish. L. H. Hall and L. B. Kier, Bull. Environm. Contam. Toxicol., 32, 354 (1984)

9. Quantitative Structure-activity Relationships for Polycyclic Aromatic Hydrocarbons: Correlation Between Molecular Connectivity, Physicochemical Properties, Bioconcentration and Toxicity in Daphnia pulex. H. Govers, C. Ruepert, and H. Aiking, Chemosphere, 13, 227 (1984)

10. Molecular Connectivity: A Novel Method for Predicting Bioconcentration Factors of Hazardous Chemicals. A. Sabljic and M. Protic, Chem.-Biol. Interactions, 42, 301 (1984)

11. Toxicity and QSAR of Chlorophenols on Lebistes Reticulatus.
    J. L. Benoit-Guyod, C. Andre, G. Taillandier, J. Rochat and
    A. Boucherle, Ecotoxicol. Environ. Safety, <u>8</u>, 227 (1984)

12. Structure-activity Models of Biological Oxygen Demand.
    K. Enslein, M. Tomb and T. R. Lander, in QSAR Environ.
    Toxicol., Proc. Workshop Quant. Struct.-Act. Relat., pp 89-109,
    K. L. Kaiser, ed., Reidel, Dordrecht, Netherlands (1984)

F. Applications Using Classification Methods

1. Structure-Activity Studies of Barbiturates using Pattern Recognition Techniques. A. J. Stuper and P. C. Jurs, J. Pharm. Sci.,
   <u>67</u>, 745 (1978)

2. Classification of Drugs by Discriminant Analysis Using Fragment
   Molecular Connectivity Values. D. R. Henry and J. H. Block,
   J. Med. Chem., <u>22</u>, 465 (1979)

3. Steroid Classification by Discriminant Analysis Using Fragment
   Molecular Connectivity. D. R. Henry and J. H. Block, Eur. J.
   Med. Chem., <u>15</u>, 133 (1980)

4. Pattern Recognition of Steroids Using Fragment Molecular Connectivity. D. R. Henry and J. H. Block, J. Pharm. Sci., <u>69</u>, 1030
   (1980)

5. *Molecular Structure Influencing Either a Sweet or Bitter Taste
   among Aldoximes. L. B. Kier, J. Pharm. Sci., <u>69</u>, 416 (1980)

6. Discriminative Structural Analysis Using Pattern Recognition
   Techniques in the Structure-Taste Problem of Perillartines.
   Y. Takahashi, Y. Miashita and Y. Tanaka, J. Pharm. Sci., <u>73</u>,
   737 (1985)

G. Carcinogenesis and Mutagenesis

1. Structure-Activity Studies on Mutagenicity of Nitrosamines using Molecular Connectivity. L. B. Kier, R. J. Simons and L. H. Hall, J. Pharm. Sci., 67, 725 (1978)

2. Computer-Assisted Structure-Activity Studies of Chemical Carcinogens: A Heterogeneous Data Set. P. C. Jurs, J. T. Chou and M. Yuan, J. Med. Chem., 22, 476 (1979)

3. Computer-Assisted Structure-Activity Studies of Chemical Carcinogens: A Polycyclic Aromatic Hydrocarbon Data Set. M. Yuan and P. C. Jurs, Tox. and Appli. Pharm., 52, 294 (1980)

4. Utilization of the Index of Molecular Connectivity in the Study of Antitumor Activity of a Group of Benzo(c)fluorene Derivatives. Z. Melkova, Cesk. Farm., 33, 107 (1984)

H. Antimicrobial and Antibacterial Applications

1. *Molecular Connectivity and Substructure Analysis. L. H. Hall and L. B. Kier, J. Pharm. Sci., 67, 1743 (1978)

2. *A Comparative Analysis of Molecular Connectivity, Hansch, Free-Wilson and Darc-Pelco Methods in the SAR of Halogenated Phenols. L. H. Hall and L. B. Kier, Eur. J. Med. Chem., 13, 89 (1978)

3. *Comparison of Molecular Connectivity and Darc/Pelco Methods: Performance in Antimicrobial, Halogenated Phenol QSARS. C. Mercier and J. Dubois, Eur. J. Med. Chem., 14, 415 (1979)

4. Molecular Connectivity and Antifungal Activity. A. K. Samata, S. Ray, S. C. Basak and S. K. Bose, Arzneim.-Forsch, 32, 1515 (1982)

5. A Comparison of Log P and Molecular Connectivity in the Structure-Activity Analysis of Some Antimicrobial Agents. J. C. Boyd, J. S. Millership and A. D. Woolfson, J. Pharm. Pharmacol., 34, 158 (1982)

I. Other Applications

1. Molecular Connectivity of Muscarinic Receptor Affinity of Acetylcholine Antagonists. L. B. Kier and L. H. Hall, J. Pharm. Sci., 67, 1408 (1978)

2. Molecular Connectivity: Relations in Barbiturate Series. M. C. Bonjean and L. D. Cuong, Eur. J. Med. Chem., 13, 73 (1978)

3. Quantitative Structure-Activity Relationships and Carminative Activity II: Steric Considerations. B. K. Evans, K. C. James and D. K. Luscombe, J. Pharm. Sci., 68, 370 (1979)

4. A Systematic Approach to the Description of the Properties of Some Spinfinish Components. T. R. McGregor, Tex. Res. J., 49, 485 (1979)

5. SAR Analysis of Hydrazide Monoamine Oxidase Inhibitors Using Molecular Connectivity. A. J. Richard and L. B. Kier, J. Pharm. Sci., 69, 124 (1980)

6. SAR of Benzohydroxamic Acid Inhibitors of Ribonucleotide Reductase. B. van't Riet, L. B. Kier and H. Elford, J. Pharm. Sci., 69, 856 (1980)

7. The Relationship of Vasodilator Activity of Adenosine Analogs with Molecular Connectivity and van der Waals Volume. M. C. Bindal, P. Singh, R. P. Bhatnagar and S. P. Gupta, Arzneim.-Forsch, 30, 924 (1980)

8. Some Physicochemical Properties and Molecular Connectivity of Spasmolytic Basic Carbamates. M. Pesak, D. Zaloudkova, A. Borovansky and L. Benes, Czesk. Farm., 29, 32 (1980)

9. Molecular Connectivity Studies of Quantitative Structure-Activity of Drugs I: Quantitative Structure-Activity Relationships (QSAR) for the Central Nervous System Depressant, 2-Imidazolidinone Derivatives. E. H. Wang, F. D. Du and B. R. Xiang, Yao Hsueh Hsueh Pao, 16, 19 (1981)

10. Unit Cell and Molecular Connectivity in Tendon Collagen.. R. D. B. Fraser and T. P. Macrae, Int. J. Biol. Macromol., 3, 193 (1981)

11. Molecular Connectivity Studies on Quantitative Structure-Activity of Drugs II: Quantitative Structure-Activity Relationships (QSAR) For Leucomycins and Clindamycins. E. H. Wang, F. D. Du and B. R. Xiang, Yao Hsueh Hsueh Pao, 16, 86 (1981)

12. Molecular Connectivity and Biological Activity in a Series of Isatin Derivatives. A. Sabljic, N. Trinajstic and D. Maysinger, Acta Pharm. Jugosl., 31, 71 (1981)

13. Molecular Connectivity in Quantitative Structure-Activity Relationships Study of Ganglionic Blocking Agents of Aliphatic Amines. F. Li and Q. Zhang, Yaoxue Xuebao, 17, 592 (1982)

14. Quantitative Structure-Activity Study on the Mechanism of Inhibition of Mircrosomal p-Hydroxylation of Aniline by Alcohols. A. Sabljic and M. Protic-Sabljic, Molec. Pharm., 23, 213 (1983)

15. The Relation of Molecular Connectivity to the Structure and Properties of Nitrogen-bridged Compounds. G. Szasz, K. Novak-Hanko, L. B. Kier, I. Hermecz and J. Kokosi, Acta Pharm. Hungar., 53, 195 (1983)

16. Physicochemical and Topological Correlates of the Enzymatic Acyltransfer Reaction. S. C. Basak, D. P Gieschen, D. Harriss and V. R. Magnusson, J. Pharm. Sci., 72, 934 (1983)

17. Quantitative Structure-Activity Considerations on the Spore-inhibiting Activity of Esters of 1,3-dihydroxybutane. D. Rehn, Meth. Find. Exp. Clin. Pharmacol., 5, 701 (1983)

18. QSAR Studies on 4-Hydroxyquinoline-3-carboxylic Acids as Inhibitors of Cell Respiration Using Molecular Connectivity and van der Waals Volume. S. Gupta, Y. Prabhakar, and A. Handa, Res. Commun. Chem. Pathol. Pharmacol., 42, 455 (1983)

19. Quantitative Relationships Between Structure and Pharmacokinetic Parameters Using Molecular Connectivity Chi Indexes I. Substituted 2-Sulfapyradines. K. Reed, K. Mereish and B. Jensen, J. Pharm. Sci., 73, 237 (1984)

20. Correlation of Biological Activities of Mesoionic and Benzofused Mesoioninc Xanthine Analogs with van der Waals Volume and Molecular Connectivity. Y. S. Prabhakar, A. Handa and S. P. Gupta, J. Pharm. Dyn., 7, 366 (1984)

21. Investigation on Structure-activity Relationship in Organic Nitrates. E. Noack, Meth. Find, Exp. Clin. Pharmacol., 6, 583 (1984)

22. Structure-activity Correlations of Selected Azaarenes, Aromatic Amines, and Nitroaromatics. QSAR Environ. Toxicol., Proc. Workshop Quant. Struct.-Act. Relat., pp 337-357, K. L. Kaiser, ed. Reidel, Dordrecht, Netherlands (1984)

*Papers marked with an asterisk(*) after the number have also been listed earlier in the table under another appropriate heading.

CHAPTER 9
Future Directions
of Molecular Connectivity

In the decade since the introduction of molecular connectivity as a new and very useful structure description, a number of advances in the methodology and application have taken place. The power of molecular connectivity has advanced enormously from its origins as an alkane branching index to a paradigm capable of encoding information about both the topology and the electronic structure of complex heteroatom-containing molecules. Much of this progress has been revealed and demonstrated in previous chapters.

With each step forward, new challenges have arisen; some have been overcome while many remain. Our search for the understanding of the information resident in the indexes, the proper choice of delta values, the necessary changes in the algorithm, the new applications and the mathematical treatments of the results continues. We devote this last chapter to an elaboration of some of the current, unsolved problems with a brief description of our ideas on how each may be approached. It is our hope that a decade from now, many of these will have found their way into the main stream of QSAR analyses.

1. The Algorithm for ^2X

In chapter four, the information in the value of ($^mX - {}^mX^v$) was demonstrated in several ways. In particular, this index was found to encode information about the non-sigma electrons in a molecule plus the topology of adjacent atoms. Specifically the value of the index ($^0X-^0X^V$) describes the non-sigma electrons while ($^1X - ^1X^V$) describes the same electrons plus the topology of all α atoms. The problem with the ($^2X - ^2X^V$) index is that not all of the bond terms making up this value are composed of atoms β to a heteroatom or double bond. As an example, in formulating ($^2X - ^2X^V$) for diethylamine, the following dissection leads to the fragments:

$$\text{(a)} \qquad \text{(b)} \qquad \text{(c)}$$

The fragments (a) and (c) carry information about the topology of the heteroatom and skeletal atoms β to it. The (b) fragment carries information only about the heteroatom and α skeletal atoms. The (b) fragment contains information similar to that in the ($^1X - ^1X^V$) index. The (b) fragment adds numerically to (^2X and $^2X^V$) but is not derived from the α , β heteroatom structure. To rectify this redundancy, it may be necessary to reformulate the algorithm for ^2X (or $^2X^V$) so that only the terminal delta values in the product ($\delta_i \, \delta_j \, \delta_k$) are specified. Thus ^2X may be better calculated from the expression:

$$^2X = \Sigma \; (\; \delta_i \; \delta_k \;)^{-0.5}$$

where δ_i and δ_k are the terminal atoms in all 2-path fragments. With this approach the (b) fragment would disappear from the summation. The question then can be asked, is the formulation of ^2X, ^3X etc. by this method superior to the current method? Studies along these lines should be informative.

2.   The δ^V Value for Fluorine

The first use of δ^V values for the halogens were empirically derived. They were based on the contributions of the halogens to the molar refractions of halobenzenes. From this it was proposed that $\delta^V(F) = -20$. If δ^V is based on the expression $Z^V - h$, $\delta^V(F)$ should be 7. The latter value is useful for electronic information while the former value leads to indexes capable of describing the volume related properties of fluorides. In the estimation of the Mulliken electronegativity, X_M, of fluorine from the expression:

$$X_M = 2.05 \ (\ \delta^V - \delta \ ) + 6.99$$

a value for $\delta^V(F)$ of about 3.5 would be reasonable.

Complicating the problem is the fact that F is probably not hybridized sp^3 when covalently bonded. This makes the molecule unique in comparison to the other atoms commonly encountered in organic molecules. It raises the question as to the real meaning of δ^V and $\delta^V - \delta$ for this atom. Further study is necessary to accurately describe fluorine in a variety of circumstances.

3. Valence Delta Values for Third Quantum Level Atoms

In Chapter 1 we have described the derivation of δ^V values for 3rd and higher quantum level atoms in their valence state. Using the expression:

$$\delta^V = (Z^V - h) \ / \ (Z - Z^V - 1)$$

the δ^V values for second quantum level atoms in their valence states appear to describe their structure fairly well for both volume-related and electronic properties. The same expression also appears to account for the volume-related properties of atoms in the 3rd quantum level, as for example the molar refraction. The electronic properties such as electronegativity, however, are not well accounted for. As an example, the Kier/Hall electronegativity, described in Chapter 4, calculated from $\delta^V - \delta$, is a negative number for 3rd quantum level atoms. To bring these atom electronegativities into line with carbon, nitrogen and oxygen, we have had to use an alternate description, namely $(\delta^V - \delta)/N^2$ where N is the quantum number. At this level, the volume-related and electronic structures present a dualism that cannot be accommodated into one expression. We are currently studying this problem.

4. Valence Deltas for Higher Oxidation States

In chapter 1, we have described the empirical derivation of the δ^V values for sulfur in the -SO- and -SO$_2$- fragments and for phosphorus in the -P=O fragment. These moieties frequently occur in biologically important molecules; hence some systematic way to describe them in the context of molecular connectivity is desirable. From the expression $(Z^V - h)/(Z - Z^V - 1)$ the denominator is 9 for sulfur and phosphorus. The empirical δ^V values for the oxidation states for each, expressed as fractions of 9, are: S in -S-S- is 8/9; S in -SO- is 12/9; S in -SO$_2$- is 24/9; and P in -PO is 20/9. The question arises as to the significance of the numerator in each case. How do these numerators relate to $Z^V - h$ in the general expression for δ^V? More importantly, are these values the best in terms of describing the structure in a meaningful and consistent way? Current studies are addressing this problem.

5. Molecular Shape

It has been proposed (Kier and Hall, 1976) that the normalized index $^1X/n$ where n is the number of atoms, carries information of relative shape. The expression permits a comparison across isomeric series. The values of $^1X/n$ have limits of 0.400 - 0.500 for non-cyclic molecules. The treatment of cyclic molecules in this way does not give compatible results.

There is no doubt that the question of molecular shape is an extremely important one, particularly with the advent of computer graphic visualization of receptor and enzyme active sites. The use of $^1X/n$ is probably inadequate since it is based on the branching influence only and it does not deal adequately with cyclic molecules. The problem has recently been considered by Kier (1985) who has departed from formal molecular connectivity and has devised a model with limiting structures which carries information about an attribute which can be defined as shape. The model is based on the assignment of star and linear graphs as limiting shapes for any isomeric series. All molecules in that isomeric series then fall somewhere between these limits. To describe these limiting structures, and all intermediate structures, the count of the number of 2-path (3-contiguous atoms) fragments is made. This value, ^2P_i, for molecule i is then compared to the limiting structures for the isomeric series, $^2P_{max}$ for the star graph and $^2P_{min}$ for the straight chain graph. The final expression for the shape index, ^2K:

$$^2K = 2\ ^2P_{max}\ ^2P_{min}/(^2P_i)^2$$

describes a molecular shape attribute which is a quantification of relative star-likeness and straight chain-likeness.

Further refinements have been made to account for the different shape contributions from heteroatoms and carbon atoms other than sp^3 hybrids. More progress is anticipated in this new generation of molecular structure descriptors.

6. A Chemical Reaction Index for Information Storage

Using valence connectivity indexes of the first order Mosby and Kier (1980) have described a general approach to the numerical description of a chemical reaction for purposes of information storage and retrieval. The derivation of the index for a particular reaction is simply the difference between $^1X^V$ (reactant) and $^1X^V$ (product), each expressed in the most general chemical notation.

Every chemical reaction can be written out as a transformation of a reactant, expressed in general form, and a product also expressed in general form. As an example, if we wish to numerically encode the reaction or process of the transformation of an ester to an alcohol, the general expression is:

$$R-CH_2-(CO)-O-CH_2-R \longrightarrow R-CH_2-OH$$

The $^1X^V$ indexes are calculated (assuming $\delta^V = 0$ for the R groups). For the general ester formula $^1X^V = 1.050$ and for the general alcohol formula $^1X^V = 0.316$. An index to encode the process or reaction, ester $\rightarrow$ alcohol, is derived from the expression $^1X^V$ product) $- {}^1X^V$ (reactant). In this case, the index $\Delta {}^1X^V$ is -0.734.

By uniformly writing down general formulae for products and reactants, any reaction can be described by a single number. The utility of this method lies in the ability to store or recall information under a single number which can be derived unambiguously from the generalized formulae for any reaction. The index can be quickly calculated; thus no tables need be consulted to obtain the index. Further refinements of this information system will expand its value.

7. Structure Interpretation from Combinations of Chi Indexes

In Chapters three and four it was shown that the connectivity indexes are based on significant structure information. The simple chi indexes ^mX_t are based on the connections in the molecular skeleton without regard to atom type. The molecular topology is represented by the simple indexes. Degree of branching is ranked by both ^1X and ^2X. The ^3X_p index contains information on molecular flexibility and the $^4X_{pc}$ index contains structure information on ring isomers and crowding in substituted alicyclic skeletons. On the other hand the valence indexes $^mX_t^V$ contain specific information on the atom identities and valence electron structure. This information may be called the electronic topology of the molecule.

The sum of the simple and valence delta values for $-XH_n-$ skeletal groups relates to their van der Waals' volume. The difference of the delta values is related to the valence state electronegativity of covalently bonded atoms. It would be quite helpful if these two types of information could be separated so that they could be independently represented in QSAR equations.

Preliminary steps have been taken to extract these two types of information from the chi indexes. In chapter two, section 6B, on the analysis of van der Waals a and b parameters the sum and difference of chi indexes were introduced. It was shown that combinations such as $^1X + {}^1X^V$ and $^0X + {}^0X^V$ correlate very significantly with the b parameter which is known to represent molecular volume. For the present we suggest that the molecular size aspects of structure may be represented by the sum of pairs of simple and valence chi indexes:

$$\text{Molecular Size} \rightarrow {}^mX_t + {}^mX_t^V$$

An example using the combined indexes in a biological study is given in Chapter six, section A.

Molecular electronic structure is represented in both simple and valence chi indexes. However, because of the definition of the delta value used in the simple indexes only the sigma electron network of the molecular skeleton is encoded in the simple chi indexes, ${}^mX_t^V$ Therefore, when ${}^mX_t^V$ is subtracted from ${}^mX_t^V$, the contribution of the sigma electrons is subtracted out. There remains only the electronic structure of the nonsigma (pi and lone pair) electrons.

Preliminary work with difference chi indexes indicates the possible development of useful electronic indexes. In Chapter three, section 6B, the van der Waals a parameter is shown to relate to $^1X^V - {}^1X$. More dramatically, it is shown in Chapter four, section 8B, that difference variables correlate very significantly with ionization potentials of alcohols, ethers and amines (one data set). It has also been shown that measures of aromaticity may be represented in terms of $^1X^V - {}^1X$ as a "benzene-like" index. These three properties are directly related to the electronic structure of the nonsigma electrons. It is suggested that consideration be given to the use of chi difference variables for representation of the electronic properties of the nonsigma electrons.

Molecular electronic properties
of pi and lone pair electrons $\longrightarrow$ $^{m}X_{t}^{v} - {}^{m}X_{t}$

8. Direct Use of Sum and Difference Delta Values in Chi Indexes

The direct use of the sum and difference delta values in the chi algorithm may lead to interesting and useful results. A new set of topological indexes using, for example, two first order indexes could be defined as follows:

$$^{1}X^{s} = \Sigma \; (\delta_{i}^{s} \delta_{j}^{s})^{-0.5}$$

$$^{1}X^{d} = \Sigma \; (\delta_{i}^{d} \delta_{j}^{d})^{-0.5}$$

The delta values with the superscripts s and d stand for the sum and difference delta values. Defined in this manner, the $^{m}X^{s}$ indexes carry information based on molecular size and the $^{m}X^{d}$ indexes encode information on electronegativity.

One preliminary study has been done using these new indexes with the van der Waals parameter data used in chapter two, section 6B. With the first order index based on the sum of delta values, the following equation is found:

$$b = 0.0918\,^{1}X^{s} + 0.0290$$
$$r = 0.968, \; s = 0.011, \; F = 1041, \; n = 71$$

When the zeroth order index is added to the equation,

$$b = 0.0340\,^{0}X^{s} + 0.0214\,^{1}X^{s} + 0.00940$$
$$r = 0.983, \; s = 0.0085, \; F = 973, \; n = 71$$

The addition of the second order index lowers the standard deviation to 0.0080. These results are of the same quality as given in chapter two. This is a preliminary study but the quality of the results suggest that this may be a fruitful approach.

9. Connectivity Indexes and Property Estimations

Molecular connectivity was developed to provide indexes of molecular structure for use in biological QSAR. As a matter of general interest, however, examination of relations to physicochemical properties were undertaken by several investigators. (See Chapter 8.) Chapters 2, 3 and 4 summarize some of the studies of property relationships. Since the ability to estimate physicochemical properties is of increasing importance, especially in environmental and engineering applications, it is of more than passing interest to investigate further the potential of chi indexes for this purpose.

Lyman (1982) has provided an extensive compilation of methods for estimation of organic compound properties. The use of chi indexes is cited for many properties, including those mentioned in this book. The references cited, however, do not reflect later developments in the use of molecular connectivity. There is, at this time, reason to expect improved results for estimation when use is made of the discussions in this book.

For a series of related molecules chi indexes, both simple and valence, provide the basis for excellent correlation of many properties. It remains to be seen just how much diversity in molecular structure sets can be accommodated. With the increasing availability of data bases and the use of a computer program for chi indexes, the employment of connectivity could prove very useful. Further, the ideas presented in the previous two sections also provide encouragement in seeking property estimations from combinations of chi indexes.

256

References

Kier, L. B. and Hall, L. H. (1976). <u>Molecular Connectivity in Chemistry and Drug Research</u>. Academic, New York.

Kier, L. B. (1985). A shape index from molecular graphs. Quant. Struct.-Act. Relat., in press.

Lyman, W. (1982). <u>Handbook of Chemical Property Estimation Methods</u>. McGraw-Hill Book Co., New York.

Mosby, M. and Kier, L. B. (1980). Method for generating a chemical reaction index for storage and retrieval of information. J. Chem. Inf. Comp. Sci., <u>20</u>, 217-221.

Author Index

Acton,E.M., 209,213
Agin,D., 28
Allen,T.L., 6
Amidon,G., 10
Amoore,J.E., 159
Anik,S.T., 10
Bard,J., 104
Barlow,R.B., 31,197,199
Battaglia,M., 99
Bawden,D., 10
Berger,F.M., 153
Bevington,P.R., 104,111,119,123
Block,J., 174
Bondi,A., 46
Brillouin,L., 163
Costello,R., 135
Daniel,C., 104,111,114,119,
    122-123
DiPaolo,T., 164-165,189
Dove,S., 173-174
Dunn,W., 173
Carter,D.V., 161
Draper,N., 104
Driesbach,R.R., 26
Edward,J.T., 31
Exner,O., 84,87
Fajans,K., 6
Foks,H., 33-34
Franke,R., 173-174
Franklin,J.F., 6
Freund,R.J., 104
Fujita,T., 158
Fulcrand,P., 207
Gardner,R.J., 186
Glennon,R.J., 151
Gray,H.L., 138

Hall,L.H., 11,12,15,16,29,35,
    38,39,46,48,50,58,63-64,
    71,84,128,134-135,153,
    159,161,165,192,200,217,
    250
Hammett,L.D., 161
Hansch,C., 158,219
Henry,D., 174
Hermann,R., 48
Hinze,J., 71,74,81
Huheey,J.E., 79
Ickikawa,Y., 108
Jaffe,H.H., 71,74,81
Julg,A., 97
Jurs,P., 174
Kaliszan,K., 33
Kier,L.B., 11,12,15,16,35,38,
    39,46,48,50,58,63-64,71,
    84,128,134-135,148,151,
    153,159,161-162,165,174,
    192,200,207,209,217,250-251
Klages,F., 6,49
Klarmann,E.G., 158
Klett,C.J., 104
Koch,R., 185
Laidler,K., 6
Lee,M.L., 33
Lewis,D., 94
Littel,R.C., 104
Luisi,P.L., 58
Lyman,W., 255
Mager,P., 166
Mann,G., 56-58
Martin,Y., 173
Millership,J.S., 32
Mosby,M., 251

Mulliken,R., 71
Neter,J., 104
Overall,J.E., 104
Pauling,L., 6,16,70
Peters,D.,94
Phipps,G., 134
Randic,M., 8,11
Rao,C.R., 104
Richard,A., 165,207
Richie,G., 99
Roche,M., 97
Sanderson,R.T., 75,79
Schucany,W.R., 138
Schultz,T., 214
Shannon,C.E., 162
Somayajulu,G.R., 6
Stone,H., 209,213
Spivakovskii,G.I., 32
Stupor,A., 174
Tamm,I., 217
Topliss,J., 135
Vogel,A., 6,19
Wasserman,W., 104
Watanabe,K., 100
Weaver,W., 162
White,C., 33
Wold,A., 173
Wood,F., 104,111,114,122-123
Woolfson,A.D., 32
Yamano,T., 108
Zwolinski,B.J., 6

Subject Index

Activity measure, 107,184
Additivity, 4,76,78
Adjacency, 7,8,11,17,53
  ring, 61
Alcohols:
  chromatography, 34
  flavor, 186-189
  heat of atomization, 35
  heat of vaporization, 36
  ionization potential, 100
  magnetic susceptibility, 38
  molar volume, 48
  water solubility, 29
Aldehydes, flavor, 186-189
Aldoximes, 209-214
Alkanes:
  branching, 55-56
  branching index, 8
  chromatography, 32
  density, 56-57
  flexibility index, 58-60
  general anesthetics, 189-192
  heat of vaporization, 37
  Mann Z_g values, 56-58
  molar refraction, 26
Alkyl benzenes:
  molar refraction, 27
  chi indexes, 62
Amphetamines, 200-207
Analysis of variance, 106,114-115
  basic theorem, 106
  correlation coefficient, 115
  multiple linear regression, 116,
    133
  simple linear regression, 115
ANOVA (*See* Analysis of variance)

Anosmia, fatty acids, 64
Amino acid volume, 49
Antiviral agents, 64,217-222
Antimicrobial agents, 153-155
Aromaticity, 94-99
Aspirgilus niger, 161
Benzene-likeness, 94-99
  criteria, 95
  index, 96-99
Benzimidazoles, 64,217-222
Bitter taste, 209-214
Bioconcentration factor, 185
Boiling point, 10
Branching, 8-9, 43-44, 55
  degree, 43
  adjacency, 10
Branching index, 8-9
CFUNC, 146,220
Chance correlations, 128,134-138
  (*See also* Random numbers)
Chemical reaction index, 251-252
Chi index, 11
  chain, 14, 148,150
  cluster, 14,146,148-149
  first order, 13,43-50,76,96
    147,149
  fourth order, 59,61-63
  higher order, 13,63-64
  index selection, 145-150
  linear combinations, 39-40
  path, 13-14, 53,58,146
    148-149,155,219
  path/cluster, 14,59-61
    146-149,155-156
  second order, 13,50-52,247-248
  simple, 12

260

third order, 53-59,65
valence, 15
zero order, 14,147,149
Chromatography, 32-35
alcohols, 34
alkanes, 32
polyaromatic hydrocarbons, 33
pyrazine carbothioamides, 33
Conformation, 53-55
Connection, 4,7
Connectivity computer program (see
CFUNC)
Connectivity matrix, 7
Constituitive property, 4
Correlation coefficient, 116,132
137,140 (See also Statistics)
Cytochrome P-450 conversion, 108
Degrees of freedom, 105-106, 114-
115,117,120,124
Delta value, 11,15,44-46
simple, 11,45,69-76
sum/difference, 46-47,70-76,254
third quantum level atoms, 18-19,
249-250
valence, 15,17,19,20,46,
69-76,203,248-250
expression, 15,18
Density, 56-57
Discriminant analysis, 173-179,
209-214
Electronegativity, 70-76
benzene substituent value, 80-88
equalization, 75-78
group values, 79-88
Kier/Hall, 73-74,79,249
Mulliken, 70-75,249
orbital, 81-82
Pauling, 70-71,164
valence state, 70-75
Electrons:
lone pair, 16,17,46,69-75
core, 18
nonsigma, 76-79,89,95,99,170,
247-248,253
pi orbital, 17,46,69-75
sigma orbital, 18,46,69-75
valence, 15,18,69,75
Ethers:
general anesthetics, 189-192
heat of atomization, 35
ionization potential, 100
molar volume, 48

toxicity, 64
Flexibility index, 58,60
Flavor threshold, 186-189
Fluorine, delta value, 16-17,248
Fluorophosphates, 166-173
Fragment:
chi index, 52-53
term, 13,53-55,153-156,201,
217-222,248
Gaussian model, 159
General anesthetics, 189-192
Halucinogenic potency, 200-207
Hammett parameters, 83-88,161
Heat of atomization, 35-36
alcohols, 35
ethers, 35
thiols, 35
Heat of vaporization, 36-37
alcohols, 36
alkanes, 37
Heteroatoms, 16,19,95-100,217,
248
delta values, 16,18,19,20
substituents, 148-150
Hybrid state (see valence state)
Hydrogen bonding, 123,153,165
Hydrogen suppression, 4,11,15
Hyper/hypoglycemia, 174-179
Hyperbolic model, 119,122,157-
158,187-188,189-192
Indicator variable, 123,164-165
Internal energy, vaporization:
definitions, 36
alkanes, 37
Information content, 162-164
Ionization potential, 71,100-101
Jackknife method, 138-139
Ketones:
flavor threshold, 186-189
general anesthetics, 189-192
Least squares:
linear, 108-119
intercept, 108,112,116
slope, 108,112,116
Student t, 114
multiple linear, 119,121,
123-127
residuals, 111
standard deviation, 114
Linear combination, chi indexes,
174, 252-254
difference, 40,99-101,168-173

electronic property, 40,169-170
  sum, 39,168-173
  volume relation, 39,169
Linear model, 107-120
LSD, 151-152
Magnetic susceptibility, 37-38
  alcohols, 38
  definition, 37
Matrix:
  connectivity, 7
  distance, 7
Mescalines, 204-205
Models, 103,107,117,119,121,123,134
  linear, 108-119
  multivariate, 123
  nonlinear, 107
  selection, 127-128
  (*See also* Parabolic model,
    Hyperbolic model)
Molar refraction, 26-28,50-52
  alkanes, 26
  alkylbenzenes, 27
Molecular connectivity, 10-20
  calculation, 21-22
  delta values, 15-20
  index, 12,75-76
    extended, 12
    simple, 12
  terms, 12-14
    chain, 13
    cluster, 13
    path, 13
    path/cluster, 13
Molecular negentropy, 163
Molecular shape, 250
Molecular size, 44
Molecular structure, 1-4,10-12,128
  aromaticity, 94
  conformation, 53-56
  degree of branching, 43-44
  electronic, 76-79
  flexibility, 58-59
  heteroatoms, 16-19,50
  ring substituents, 61-63
  unsaturation, 15,50
Molecular surface area, 48,51
Molecular symmetry, 161-164
Molecular topography, 3-4,6,69
Molecular topology, 3-8
Molecular volume, 44-47
Monoamine oxidase inhibitors,
  207-209

Muscarinic agents:
  agonists, 198
  antagonists, 192-198
  bulky group, 197
  onium group, 196
Nonlinear models, 121-123,156-159
Odor similarity, 159
Outlier, 117-118,122
Parabolic model, 119,121,156,
  158-159,166,171,187
Phenols, 108-109,124-126
  cytochrome P-450 conversion,
    108-110
  S.typhosa, 158
  toxicity, 128-142
Phenylpropyl ethers, 153-156
Polarizability, 28
Polarographic half wave
  potential, 207-209
Polyaromatic hydrocarbons, 33
Principal component analysis,
  148-150
Property estimation, 25-26,255
QSAR, 1,28,103,128,130,138,
  147,150,173,183,217
  data selection, 184
  interpretation, 185-192,195,
    201-207,210-213,219-222
Quadratic model (see *Parabolic
  model*)
Regression, 108-135
  index selection, 145-150
  linear (see *Least squares*)
  multiple linear, 119-127
  stepwise, 130
  (*See also* Least squares)
Random numbers, 135,139,194-197,
  200-201
Reciprocal square root, 9,75-76
S.typhosa, 158
Scatter plot, 108
Skeletal branching term, 36
Solubility (in water), 29-30
  alcohols, 29
  halobenzenes, 29
Solvent polarity, 88-93
  index, 90-93
  measurement, 92-93
Sorption coefficient, 185
Statistics, 103-126
  average, 104
  correlation coefficient, 116

definitions, 104-105
degrees of freedom, 104-105,127
deviation, 104
F statistic, 116-117,119-120,
    122,127,131,135-136
residuals, 111-113,122,126,142
standard deviation, 114,141
Student t, 114
sum of squares, 104,111
variance, 105
Structure abbreviation, 150-152
Structure information, 43,89,252-
    254
Substructure analysis, 152-156,
    217-222
Sweet taste, 209,214
Thiols, heat of vaporization, 35
Toluenesulfonylureas, 174-179
Topological index, 8
Total surface optimization, 165-173
Toxicity:
  guppy, 185
  heterocycles, 214-217
Tree graph, 7
Tricophyton mentagrophytes, 153
Unsaturation, 15,50,213
Valence, 15-16
  deltas (see *Delta value*)
Valence state, 69-71
Van der Waals constants, 38-40,
    254-255
  volume dependence, 39
  electronic property, 40
Van der Waals radius, 44,46,48,
    50-51
Variable selections, 130,145-150
Variance ratio (see *statistics*)

RETURN TO: CHEMISTRY LIBRARY
100 Hildebrand Hall • 510-642-3753

LOAN PERIOD 1	2 _1 Month_	3
4	5	6

ALL BOOKS MAY BE RECALLED AFTER 7 DAYS.

Renewals may be requested by phone or, using GLADIS, type **inv**
followed by your patron ID number.

DUE AS STAMPED BELOW.

FORM NO. DD 10   UNIVERSITY OF CALIFORNIA, BERKELEY
3M 7-08   Berkeley, California 94720–6000